# THE SCOTTISH FOOTBALL
# QUIZ BOOK

# THE SCOTTISH FOOTBALL QUIZ BOOK

**Compiled by Graeme Ross**

**Forewords by John Wark and Alex McLeish**

APEX PUBLISHING LTD

First published in hardback in 2009 by

Apex Publishing Ltd

PO Box 7086, Clacton on Sea, Essex, CO15 5WN, England

www.apexpublishing.co.uk

Copyright © 2009 by Graeme Ross
The author has asserted his moral rights

British Library Cataloguing-in-Publication Data
A catalogue record for this book
is available from the British Library

ISBN:        1-906358-35-4        978-1-906358-35-8

Typeset in 10.5pt Chianti Bdlt Win95BT

Cover Design: Siobhan Smith

Printed and bound in Great Britain by the
MPG Books Group, Bodmin and King's Lynn

# FOREWORD

Although I never had the pleasure of playing in the Scottish leagues, I was honoured by my country on 29 occasions and played in the 1982 World Cup Finals. Therefore, I was delighted to be asked to write the foreword to The Scottish Football Quiz Book. Most people love a quiz, and footballers are no exception. I know that my old Ipswich and Scotland team mate George Burley in his capacity as Scotland Coach will love this book. We could certainly have used it to good effect in all those long motorway coach journeys with Ipswich! Graeme has packed a multitude of fascinating facts and figures into his book, and the questions will provide a keen test of the reader's knowledge.

So, whether you support Aberdeen or Annan Athletic, or are simply a member of the Tartan Army, I can thoroughly recommend The Scottish Football Quiz Book to all followers of Scottish Football.

I hope you enjoy the book, I certainly did!

### John Wark

*Won 29 Caps for Scotland*

# FOREWORD

Having played for and coached the Scotland international side, and played for and managed some of Scottish Football's finest clubs, I was delighted to be asked to write the foreword to The Scottish Football Quiz Book.

This is a book that every student of Scottish football will enjoy immensely. With 1,000 questions on a huge range of subjects, there is something here for everyone, and I can guarantee that you will be entertained and fascinated by the wealth of facts and figures to be found in Graeme's challenging book. And it's not just fans of the big clubs who are catered for – there are questions on every senior club in Scotland, as well as the National side, and many of the great characters who have graced the football world.

Reading through the book reminded me of many of great players Scotland has produced – even the ones that kicked me! Perhaps I can educate my Birmingham Sassenachs on the team bus!

Enjoy the book, I certainly did!

**Alex McLeish**

*Won 77 Caps for Scotland and managed Scotland in 2007*

# INTRODUCTION
## By Graeme Ross

Scottish football has experienced many highs and lows over the decades and in the current economical climate the Scottish game faces an uncertain future. Whatever happens in the future however, nothing can detract from our glorious past as a football nation.

Hopefully this Scottish Football Quiz Book will remind the readers of some of the great achievements by our teams and wonderful footballers and managers. As a nation we have given so much to the football world, and long may it continue.

I would like to thank John Wark and Alex McLeish for writing the forewords to the book and everyone who provided a few lines in support of the book. Thanks are also due to John Riddle for suggesting the idea in the first place and introducing me to Chris Cowlin and Apex Publishing Ltd. Thanks to Chris for all his help and support.

Finally as always, a special word of thanks to my wife Ann and my family for all their patience and understanding.


*Best wishes*
**Graeme Ross**

www.apexpublishing.co.uk

# BEGINNINGS

*These Scottish internationals of the 1970s and 1980s all found success in England after beginning their careers in the Scottish League. Can you match each player with his first club?*

| | | |
|---|---|---|
| 1. | Joe Jordan | St Mirren |
| 2. | Gary Gillespie | Clyde |
| 3. | Alan Hansen | Dumbarton |
| 4. | Steve Nicol | Dunfermline Athletic |
| 5. | Gordon McQueen | Morton |
| 6. | Pat Nevin | Partick Thistle |
| 7. | George Wood | Ayr United |
| 8. | Allan Evans | Hibernian |
| 9. | Graeme Sharp | East Stirling |
| 10. | Alex Cropley | Falkirk |

# SCOTLAND AT THE WORLD CUP

11.    Scotland opened the 1998 World Cup finals against which nation?

12.    Which midfielder scored a double against New Zealand in the 1982 tournament?

13.    Who was Scotland's captain in the 1978 tournament?

14.    How many Leeds United players were in the 1974 finals squad of 22?

15.    Following on from the above question, how many can you name?

16.    Who is the only Scottish footballer to have scored in three World Cup finals tournaments?

17.    Which player scored twice for Peru against Scotland in the 1978 World Cup?

18.    How many times have Scotland played Brazil in the World Cup finals?

19.    In the 1954 tournament Scotland lost 7-0 against which country?

20.    Who was Scotland's manager at the 1986 World Cup tournament?

# ABERDEEN

21. How many times have Aberdeen won the Scottish Cup?

22. Who scored Aberdeen's goals when they won the European Cup Winners' Cup in 1983?

23. True or false: Aberdeen beat Rangers 6-0 in the 1954 Scottish Cup semi-final?

24. Which side did Aberdeen beat in the final of the European Super Cup in 1983?

25. What significant change did the club make to their playing kit just prior to the outbreak of World War II?

26. Who is the only Aberdeen player to have scored a hat-trick for Scotland?

27. Which current Aberdeen player's father played for the Dons in the 1980s?

28. Who scored Aberdeen's winning goal in the 1976 Scottish League Cup final?

29. Who is Aberdeen's record goalscorer?

30. What was the score in Aberdeen's first European tie in 1967 against KR Reykjavik?

# LEGENDS – DENIS LAW

31. **Where was Denis born?**

32. **Can you name Denis's three English clubs?**

33. **True or false: Denis won a European Cup Winners medal?**

34. **In how many World Cup finals tournaments did Denis play?**

35. **In which year was Denis voted European Footballer of the Year?**

36. **For which Italian side did Denis play?**

37. **How many goals did Denis score in the international against Norway in 1963?**

38. **Against which country did Denis win his final cap?**

39. **And how many caps did Denis win?**

40. **How many goals did Denis score in total for Scotland?**

# AIRDRIEONIANS/AIRDRIE UNITED

41. Who was 'The Wee Prime Minister' who starred for Airdrie in the 1950s and 1960s?

42. What was Airdrieonians' famous nickname?

43. Which legendary Scottish centre forward signed for Airdrieonians in 1921?

44. In what year did Airdrie win their only Scottish Cup?

45. How many Scottish Cup finals did Airdrie reach in the 1990s?

46. Which player has scored Airdrie's only goal in European competition to date?

47. Which former Scotland international made an unsuccessful takeover bid for the club in 2001?

48. Can you name the two 'Drews' who formed a lethal striking combination for Airdrie in the 1970s?

49. Which club did Airdrie United take over to gain admittance to the Scottish League in 2003?

50. What unusual circumstances allowed Airdrie United to win promotion in 2008?

# LEGENDS – BILL SHANKLY

51. In what year was Bill born?

52. What was the full name of the junior side Bill played for – Glenbuck _____?

53. Can you name Bill's famous brother who managed Dundee and Hibernian?

54. Against which country did Bill make his international debut in 1938?

55. Bill played in two English FA Cup finals for which side?

56. With which club did Bill begin his managerial career?

57. In what year was Bill appointed Liverpool manager?

58. In what year did Bill first win the first division with Liverpool?

59. What was Bill's last trophy as a manager?

60. Finish this famous Shankly quote – 'There are only two teams in Liverpool, Liverpool and _____'.

# ALBION ROVERS

61. Which legendary manager began his playing career with Albion Rovers?

62. How many Scottish Cup finals have Rovers reached?

63. Can you name the only player capped for Scotland as an Albion Rovers player?

64. Which former Rovers player was part of The Republic of Ireland's 1990 World Cup squad?

65. Which former Rovers player is a member of the Pools Panel?

66. To the nearest five, how many managers have Albion Rovers had since World War II?

67. Which former Rovers player played against Scotland in the 1982 World Cup?

68. Following on from the above question, for which country did he play?

69. Which Rovers player of the 1980s was described by one newspaper as 'an armoured car of a winger with a cannon for a shot'?

70. Which round of the Challenge Cup did Rovers reach in season 2006/2007?

# BIRTH YEARS

*Can you match each club with their year of formation?*

| | | |
|---|---|---|
| 71. | Aberdeen | 1945 |
| 72. | Dunfermline | 1874 |
| 73. | East Stirlingshire | 1867 |
| 74. | Elgin City | 1903 |
| 75. | Hamilton Academical | 1875 |
| 76. | Hibernian | 1886 |
| 77. | Morton | 1881 |
| 78. | Motherwell | 1885 |
| 79. | Queens Park | 1893 |
| 80. | Stirling Albion | 1874 |

# ALLOA ATHLETIC

81.     What was Alloa's original club name?

82.     In which year were Alloa Athletic elected to the
        Scottish League - 1911, 1921 or 1931?

83.     Which famous Spurs and Scotland star of the 1960s
        began his career with Alloa?

84.     Do you know the name of another Scotland star who
        also began his career with Alloa and played in the
        1974 World Cup?

85.     What is the name of Alloa's home ground?

86.     How many players have been capped for Scotland as
        Alloa players?

87.     To the nearest £10,000, how much did Alloa receive
        for Martin Cameron from Bristol Rovers in 2000?

88.     Which player holds the record for the most goals in a
        season by an Alloa player?

89.     Alloa reached the second division play-offs in season
        2007/2008. How did they fare?

90.     Alloa's record victory of 9-0 was achieved in 2005,
        against which team?

# HOME GROUNDS

*Can you match the grounds with the teams that play there?*

| | | |
|---|---|---|
| 91. | Albion Rovers | Ochilview |
| 92. | Arbroath | East End Park |
| 93. | Ayr United | Stark's Park |
| 94. | Cowdenbeath | Cliftonhill |
| 95. | Dunfermline Athletic | Rugby Park |
| 96. | Kilmarnock | McDiarmid Park |
| 97. | Raith Rovers | Stair Park |
| 98. | St Johnstone | Central Park |
| 99. | Stenhousemuir | Gayfield |
| 100. | Stranraer | Somerset Park |

# ANNAN ATHLETIC

101. In which year were Annan Athletic formed – 1932, 1942 or 1952?

102. Who were Annan's opponents in their first ever Scottish League match?

103. Following on from the above question, what was the score in the match?

104. What is the name of Annan's ground?

105. Which other club has Annan's manager Harry Cairney managed?

106. Which current Scottish first division manager was formerly manager of Annan?

107. Which former Gretna and Motherwell player became assistant manager at Annan in 2008?

108. Which player scored Annan's first goal in the Scottish League?

109. In which county of Scotland is Annan based?

110. What colours are Annan's jerseys?

# CLUB NICKNAMES

*Can you match the nicknames with the clubs?*

| | | |
|---|---|---|
| 111. | Alloa Athletic | The Pars |
| 112. | Arbroath | The Buddies |
| 113. | Clyde | The Doonhamers |
| 114. | Dumbarton | The Arabs |
| 115. | Dundee United | The Wasps |
| 116. | Dunfermline Athletic | The Jags |
| 117. | East Fife | The Red Lichties |
| 118. | Partick Thistle | The Sons |
| 119. | Queen of the South | The Fifers |
| 120. | St Mirren | The Bully Wee |

# ARBROATH

121. Arbroath hold the record victory in world senior football. What was the score?

122. Following on from the above question, in what year was this victory achieved?

123. Coincidentally, there was a similar score in another match on the same day as Arbroath's record victory. What was it?

124. Which player scored 13 goals in Arbroath's record victory?

125. Which club are Arbroath's keenest local rivals?

126. Which player, who scored the winner in a 1990s Scottish Cup final, became Arbroath's manager in 2003?

127. Who is Arbroath's most capped player?

128. Name the three members of Rangers' European Cup Winners' Cup squad of 1972 who moved on to Arbroath.

129. Which team did Arbroath beat in the 2007/2008 play-offs to win promotion to the second division?

130. What is Arbroath's ground's major claim to fame?

# NAME THE YEAR

131. Graeme Souness became manager of Rangers.

132. Gretna were elected to the Scottish League.

133. George Best signed for Hibs.

134. Celtic celebrated their centenary by winning the League and Scottish Cup 'double'.

135. Third Lanark went out of existence.

136. Livingston won the CIS League Cup.

137. Fergus McCann took control of Celtic.

138. Martin O'Neill became manager of Celtic.

139. Motherwell won the Scottish Cup for the first time.

140. Maurice Johnston signed for Rangers.

# AYR UNITED

141. From which Robert Burns poem does Ayr United's nick name come?

142. And what is Ayr's famous nickname?

143. In what year did Ayr United reach their only major Cup final?

144. Following on from the above question, which team did they play in the final?

145. Following on from the above, who was Ayr's manager at the time?

146. Which former Ayr United manager is the oldest player to play in a British professional match?

147. How many goals did Jimmy Smith score for Ayr in season 1927/1928?

148. Can you name the Ayr player who was capped by Scotland in 1975 before moving to Celtic?

149. Which club did Gary Teale join from Ayr in 2001?

150. Can you remember the name of the lion-hearted full back of the 1960s and '70s who is Ayr's record appearance holder?

# TRIVIA - 1

151.　How many times did Airdrieonians win the B&Q Cup?

152.　Who was Martin O'Neill's first signing for Celtic?

153.　When Jim Leighton was injured in the 2000 Scottish Cup final, which outfield player replaced him?

154.　A former Motherwell manager is a nephew of Bill Shankly. Who is he?

155.　Against which team did Paul Gascoigne score his first goal for Rangers?

156.　A Motherwell player of the 1950s had the same surname as a Scottish club. Was it Dunfermline, Kilmarnock or Dundee?

157.　Which former Kilmarnock manager took over as manager of Uganda in 2008?

158.　Who was the first British player to win the European Cup with a team from outside the British Isles?

159.　Who was the first substitute to play in a first class Scottish match?

160.　What feat did Charlie Tully achieve when playing for Celtic against Falkirk in 1953?

# BERWICK RANGERS

161. Who was Berwick's manager when they knocked Rangers out of the Scottish Cup in 1967?

162. Following on from the above question, who scored the only goal in the match?

163. Which future Dundee United manager was Berwick's manager in the 1950s?

164. Which side beat Berwick 9-2 in 2008?

165. Who is Berwick's record appearance holder?

166. Can you complete the nickname of Berwick - The Bo_____s?

167. What is the name of Berwick Rangers' home ground?

168. Which former Rangers player was Berwick's manager from 1976 to 1980?

169. Who took over as Berwick's caretaker manager in 2008?

170. Which former Hearts and Falkirk manager also managed Berwick in the 1980s?

# SEASONS – 1966/1967

171. Which club reached the Fairs Cities Cup semi-final?

172. Following on from the above question, which English side defeated the Scottish club?

173. Which player was the top scorer in Celtic's European matches in this season?

174. Which player wore the number 9 jersey for Rangers in the 1967 European Cup Winners' Cup final?

175. Which team won the Scottish second division?

176. Which goalkeeper was Scottish Player of the Year for 1967?

177. Which side did Celtic knock out in the European Cup semi-final?

178. Which Celtic player conceded a penalty in the European Cup final against Inter Milan?

179. Which Rangers player captained Scotland against England in the home international at Wembley?

180. Which player scored both of Celtic's goals in their 2-0 Scottish Cup victory over Aberdeen?

# BRECHIN CITY

181. Which side did Brechin beat in the 2008 Scottish Cup only for Brechin to be thrown out of the competition for fielding two ineligible players?

182. To which club did Brechin sell Chris Templeman in 2004?

183. How many goals did Templeman score for Brechin against Stirling in October 2004?

184. Which former Brechin player has a son with the same name playing for Rangers?

185. What is the name of Brechin's home ground?

186. Brechin manager Michael O'Neill left the club in December 2008 to manage which Irish club?

187. How many times have Brechin won the Scottish second division?

188. Do you know the name of Brechin's all-time record goalscorer?

189. In which year were Brechin City formed – 1906, 1916 or 1926?

190. Brechin have two nicknames - 'City' and which other nickname?

# LEGENDS – SIR ALEX FERGUSON

191.    With which club did Sir Alex begin his playing career?

192.    Fergie joined Rangers in 1967, but from which club and what was the transfer fee?

193.    With which club did Fergie finish his playing career?

194.    Which club sacked Sir Alex in 1978?

195.    Whom did Sir Alex replace as manager of Aberdeen?

196.    How many League championships did Fergie win with Aberdeen?

197.    In what year did Sir Alex take over as Manchester United's manager?

198.    What was the first major trophy that Fergie won with Manchester United?

199.    Which legendary former Celtic player did Fergie sign in 2006?

200.    In what year did Fergie win the 'treble' – Premier League, FA Cup and Champions League - with Manchester United?

# CELTIC

201. How many Scottish League titles have Celtic won (until season 2007/2008)?

202. Who was Celtic's manager for over 40 years?

203. Seven former Celtic players are in the Scotland Hall of Fame, but how many can you name?

204. Which defender scored four goals in Celtic's famous 1966/1967 European Cup winning campaign?

205. Which goalkeeper was voted Celtic's greatest ever in 2002?

206. Following on from the above question, who was voted Celtic's greatest ever player?

207. Which Celtic legend was nicknamed 'The Mighty Atom'?

208. Which legendary manager, renowned for his quick wit and controversial career, began his playing days with Celtic in the 1940s?

209. Who scored both goals for Celtic in their Scottish Cup final win over Dundee United in 1988?

210. Which Celtic player scored six goals against Partick Thistle in a League match in 1972?

# QUOTE/UNQUOTE

*Which Scottish football persons were responsible for these pearls of wisdom?*

211. 'He's captain of Rangers, and that's one of the reasons he's captain.'

212. 'Tore's got a groin strain and he's been playing with it.'

213. 'We can beat anyone on our day, so long as we score.'

214. 'It's a Dutch invention, but we started it in Scotland.'

215. 'Our talking point this morning is George Best, his liver transplant and the booze culture in football. Don't forget, the best caller wins a crate of John Smith's.'

216. 'Everyone knows he is a crazy Celtic fan.'

217. 'That was only a yard away from being an inch-perfect pass.'

218. 'If I was English I'd top myself.'

219. 'I've been in more courts than Bjorn Borg.'

220. 'I was saying the other day, how often the most vulnerable area for goalies is between their legs.'

# CLYDE

221. In what town are Clyde based?

222. What was the name of Clyde's former ground where they played until 1986?

223. How many times have Clyde won the Scottish Cup?

224. Which two Lisbon Lions have managed the club?

225. Which former Scotland manager was in charge of Clyde for ten years?

226. Which Clyde player scored direct from a corner kick in a Scottish Cup final?

227. Which Scotland striker from the 1982 World Cup began his senior career with Clyde?

228. Which team did Clyde defeat in the 2007/2008 play-off final to retain their place in the Scottish first division?

229. Can you recall the Clyde fullback who played over 500 games for the club and won six Scotland caps?

230. Who is Clyde's most capped player?

# MACS

231. Which Mac scored nine goals in an FA Cup tie in 1971?

232. Which Mac scored twice for Aberdeen in the 1970 Scottish Cup final?

233. Which Mac scored for Scotland on his debut against Australia in 1985?

234. Can you name the Mac who scored against Lithuania in 1999?

235. Which Mac made his Scotland debut against the Czech Republic in 2008?

236. Who was the Mac who broke his leg playing for Rangers against Sporting Lisbon in 1971?

237. Which Mac, who also played for Celtic, joined Falkirk from Aberdeen in 2008?

238. Which Mac scored the winning goal for St Mirren against Rangers at Love Street in 2008?

239. Can you name the Mac who briefly managed Scotland in 1966?

240. Which Mac took over as caretaker manager at Watford in November 2008?

# TRIVIA - 2

241. Which Hibernian player scored a hat-trick against Rangers at Ibrox in 2005?

242. Who is the youngest player to have played in a Scottish Cup final?

243. Which Scottish club is the only senior club in Britain with a 'J' in its name?

244. Which Scotsman scored the winning goal in the 1980 European Cup final?

245. What was the collective term given to the Rangers defence of the 1940s and 1950s?

246. In which season did Aberdeen win their last major trophy?

247. When was the last season that both Celtic and Rangers finished outside the top two places in the League?

248. Which club has the longest senior club name in Scotland?

249. Can you name the three Scottish players who were members of Spurs' double winning side in 1961?

250. Which manager, capped 24 times for Scotland, signed Dennis Bergkamp for Arsenal?

# SEASONS – 1977/1978

251.  Which team won the domestic treble this season?

252.  Which side were runners-up in the Scottish Cup final?

253.  Which team won the Scottish first division?

254.  Who finished as top goalscorer in Scotland in this season?

255.  Who scored the two goals against Wales that took Scotland to the World Cup finals in Argentina?

256.  Following on from the above question, where was the match played?

257.  Following on again, which Wales defender was adjudged to have handled the ball against Scotland to concede a penalty in this match?

258.  In which League position did Celtic finish?

259.  Which team finished bottom of the Premier League?

260.  Which player missed a penalty against Peru in Scotland's opening match in the 1978 World Cup?

# COWDENBEATH

261. Which Scotland World Cup defender of 1990 began his career with Cowdenbeath?

262. Andy Kinnell who played for Cowdenbeath in the 1960s was a cousin of which famous Rangers and Scotland star?

263. What was the nickname of Jim Leonard, Cowdenbeath's celebrated inside forward of the 1920s?

264. What age was goalkeeper Jim McArthur when he made his Cowdenbeath debut in 1968?

265. How many spells did Andy Rolland have with Cowdenbeath as a player?

266. Cowdenbeath signed John O'Neil in 2007. How many Scottish Cup runners-up medals does John have?

267. Which Rangers and Scotland star of the 1930s was transferred to Rangers from Cowdenbeath?

268. What is the club's famous and self-deprecating nick name?

269. Which future Scotland goalkeeper had a loan spell at Cowdenbeath in 2001?

270. Who was Cowdenbeath's player/manager when they won the 3rd division in 2006?

# LEGENDS – JIMMY JOHNSTONE

271.   In what year was Jimmy born?

272.   What was Jimmy's famous nickname?

273.   Which famous English footballer was Jimmy's hero as a boy?

274.   In what year did Jimmy make his Celtic first team debut?

275.   How many Scotland caps did Jimmy win?

276.   How many goals did Jimmy score against England at Hampden in 1966?

277.   Can you name the Leeds English international fullback whom Jimmy terrorised in the 1970 European Cup semi-final?

278.   French newspaper men nicknamed Jimmy 'The Flying _____'?

279.   Which Spanish side was Celtic playing when Jimmy received a death threat?

280.   For which other Scottish League club did Jimmy briefly play?

# DUMBARTON

281. Dumbarton are one of the oldest senior sides in Scotland, but in which year were they formed?

282. Dumbarton were one of Scotland's strongest sides in the 19th century, but how many times were they first division champions?

283. In how many Scottish Cup finals have Dumbarton appeared?

284. How many times have Dumbarton won the Scottish Cup?

285. Which 'Wembley Wizard' began his career with Dumbarton in 1922?

286. Which player, later to become a famous manager, scored an own goal in a Scottish Cup semi-final when playing for Dumbarton?

287. Can you name the three brothers who played with Dumbarton in the 1980s?

288. Which ground did Dumbarton leave when they moved to their new base at Strathclyde Homes Stadium?

289. Can you name the brothers who began their career with Dumbarton in the 1970s and later played for Celtic and Rangers?

290. Which famous landmark overlooks Dumbarton's ground?

# LEGENDS – JOCK STEIN

291.  In what year was Jock Stein born?

292.  In what position did Jock play for most of his playing career?

293.  Outside of football, what was Jock's other occupation?

294.  Celtic signed Jock as a player from Llanelli Town. In which country did they play?

295.  Jock played over 200 matches for which Lanarkshire club?

296.  Which club did Jock lead as manager to the Scottish Cup in 1961?

297.  Which club did Jock leave to take the manager's job at Celtic in 1965?

298.  What was the first trophy Jock won as Celtic's manager?

299.  Which English club did Jock briefly manage?

300.  In what year did Jock become Scotland's manager?

# DUNDEE

301.  In what year were Dundee formed?

302.  In what year did Dundee win their only Scottish Cup?

303.  Which Dundee player scored six goals and then seven goals in consecutive matches?

304.  Which player signed for Dundee in 1950 for a Scottish record transfer fee?

305.  In what season did Dundee reach the European Cup semi-final?

306.  Following on from the above question, which team did Dundee play in the match?

307.  Dundee won the Scottish League Cup in season 1973/1974. Who scored the only goal of the final?

308.  Following on from the above question, who was Dundee's captain and who were Dundee's opponents in the match?

309.  When did Dundee last appear in a Scottish Cup final?

310.  Who was the famous 'White Feather' who played for Dundee?

# TRIVIA - 3

311. Which Motherwell and Ayr United goalie would often play against Celtic in a blue jersey and against Rangers in a green one?

312. In which season was the SPL formed?

313. Which former Hearts player scored West Bromwich Albion's first goal in the English Premiership in 2008/2009?

314. In season 1967/1968 Leeds United played three Scottish teams on their run to the Fairs Cities Cup final. Name them.

315. Which Rangers player scored four goals in the 1963 League Cup final?

316. Who was Hearts' manager when they won the Scottish Cup in 2006?

317. Which Dundee player scored seven goals against Queen of the South in a 10-2 victory in 1961?

318. Who was the Scottish captain of Nottingham Forest when they won the European Cup twice?

319. Which team were first division runners-up for four seasons in a row in the 1920s?

320. Which Scottish footballer scored seven goals in an FA Cup tie and finished on the losing side?

# DUNDEE UNITED

321.  Until 1923 Dundee United were known as Dundee
      _____?

322.  Can you recall United's extrovert penalty-taking
      goalkeeper from the 1970s and 1980s?

323.  Which Dundee United player became the youngest
      goalscorer in the SPL when he scored against
      Hibernian in March 2006?

324.  Who was Dundee United's manager from 1959 to
      1971?

325.  Who was the first Dundee United player to win a full
      Scotland cap?

326.  How many Scottish Cup finals have United lost?

327.  Which Spanish side did United defeat home and away
      in the Fair Cities Cup in season 1966/1967?

328.  How many major trophies did Dundee United win
      under Jim McLean's management?

329.  How many times was United legend Doug Smith
      cautioned during his playing career?

330.  Which side defeated United in the 1984 European Cup
      semi-final?

# SEASONS – 1987/1988

331. Which Celtic manager guided his side to the Scottish League and Cup double?

332. Which team did Celtic beat in the Scottish Cup final?

333. Following on from the above question, who scored Celtic's goals in the match?

334. Which Premier League side conceded exactly 100 League goals in this season?

335. Which Celtic player won both the Writers' and Players' Player of the Year Awards?

336. Which team knocked Rangers out of the Scottish Cup?

337. Which South American nation did Scotland entertain at Hampden in the Rous Cup?

338. Which team won the Scottish first division?

339. Which player scored 33 Premier League goals?

340. How many teams were relegated from the Premier League in this season?

# LEGENDS –SIR MATT BUSBY

341.  In what year was Sir Matt Busby born?

342.  For which two English clubs did Sir Matt play?

343.  In what year did Sir Matt first become Manchester United's manager?

344.  Sir Matt briefly managed Scotland in which year?

345.  What was the nickname given to Manchester United's young sides of the 1950s?

346.  As Scotland's manager Sir Matt handed which 18-year-old forward his first cap, later signing him for Manchester United?

347.  How many first division championships did Sir Matt win with Manchester United?

348.  Which team did United beat to win the European Cup in 1968?

349.  True or false: Sir Matt was never capped by Scotland as a player?

350.  In what year was Sir Matt knighted?

# DUNFERMLINE ATHLETIC

351.  Can you name Dunfermline's record appearance holder?

352.  Dunfermline reached their first major Cup final, the Scottish League Cup, in 1949, but lost to which other Fife side?

353.  Which Scottish football legend became Dunfermline's manager in 1960?

354.  Which side did Dunfermline defeat in the 1961 Scottish Cup final?

355.  Who scored twice for Dunfermline in their 3-1 victory over Hearts in the 1968 Scottish Cup final?

356.  Following on from the above question, can you name the brothers who played for Dunfermline in the match?

357.  What age was Jim Leishman when he was first appointed as Dunfermline's manager?

358.  Which Scotland international defender began his career at Dunfermline and later won a European Cup Medal in 1982?

359.  Can you remember the name of the Hungarian midfielder who made a huge impact at Dunfermline in the 1980s?

360.  Which legendary Dunfermline Athletic figure has a street in Dunfermline named after him?

# THE SCOTTISH CUP

*Can you match the teams with the years that
they won the Scottish Cup?*

361. Morton                          1924

362. Partick Thistle                 1905

363. St Mirren                       1922

364. Third Lanark                    1991

365. Motherwell                      1926

366. Dumbarton                       1895

367. Airdrieonians                   1913

368. Dundee United                   1921

369. St Bernards                     1883

370. Falkirk                         1994

# EAST FIFE

371. In what year did East Fife reach their first Scottish Cup final?

372. In what year did East Fife win the Scottish Cup?

373. Following on from the above question, which team did East Fife beat in the match?

374. How many times have the club won the Scottish League Cup?

375. Which East Fife manager of the 1940s and 1950s moved on to Rangers with great success?

376. Which East Fife player scored a hat-trick in his only appearance for Scotland?

377. Which Macedonian international signed for East Fife in 2008?

378. Who was the club's top goalscorer when they won the third division title in 2008?

379. Which prominent politician was an East Fife player in the 1970s?

380. Which East Fife player had the nicknames 'Legs' and 'Cannonball Charlie'?

# TRIVIA – 4

*Can you match these Scotland players with the number of caps that they won?*

| | | |
|---|---|---|
| 381. Danny McGrain | | 35 |
| 382. Alan Rough | | 7 |
| 383. Gordon Strachan | | 10 |
| 384. Derek Johnstone | | 50 |
| 385. Dave Narey | | 58 |
| 386. John Collins | | 50 |
| 387. Willie Miller | | 14 |
| 388. David Provan (Celtic) | | 65 |
| 389. Asa Hartford | | 62 |
| 390. Duncan Ferguson | | 53 |

# SEASONS – 1997/1998

391. Which team won the Scottish Premier League in this season?

392. Which player finished as top goalscorer in the Premier League?

393. Can you remember the Norwegian striker who scored over 20 goals for Dundee United this season?

394. Which team were relegated from the Premier League in this season?

395. Following on from the above question, which side took their place by winning the first division?

396. Which team won the Scottish Cup?

397. Who was voted Manager of the Year?

398. Which former Morton player scored twice for Scotland in a World Cup qualifier against Belarus?

399. How many points did Scotland win in the World Cup group stages?

400. Which Celtic player won the Players' Player of the Year Award?

# EAST STIRLINGSHIRE

401. To the nearest ten, how many days was Alex Ferguson the East Stirlingshire manager?

402. What was the name of Jeff Connor's book about East Stirling, published in 2005?

403. How many League points did East Stirlingshire win in season 2003/2004?

404. Which Scotland fullback of the 1960s began his career with East Stirlingshire?

405. Which ex-Celtic striker turned down the chance to become East Stirlingshire's manager in 2008?

406. What was the score when East Stirlingshire played Rangers in the 2008 Scottish Cup?

407. When was the last time East Stirlingshire played in Scotland's top division?

408. Which player was voted the BBC's East Stirlingshire Cult Hero in 2005?

409. Which Scandinavian country boasts an East Stirlingshire fan club?

410. By what name were East Stirlingshire known for one season in the 1960s?

# LEGENDS – KENNY DALGLISH

411. Which Celtic manager signed Kenny for the club?

412. To the nearest ten, how many League goals did Kenny score for Celtic?

413. Against which country did Kenny make his Scotland debut in 1971?

414. Which manager awarded Kenny his first cap?

415. In how many World Cups did Kenny play?

416. Can you recall the transfer fee when Kenny moved from Celtic to Liverpool?

417. How many Scotland caps did Kenny win?

418. How many goals did Kenny score for Scotland?

419. With whom does Kenny share the Scotland goalscoring record?

420. Which team did Kenny support as a boy?

# ELGIN CITY

421. In what year were Elgin elected to the Scottish League?

422. In 1968 Elgin reached the Scottish Cup quarter-final, when they were knocked out by which side?

423. Which former Dundee United and Gretna goalkeeper was born in Elgin and began his career with Elgin City?

424. Do you know the name of the striker who played for Elgin in the 1980s and later scored the winning goal for Scotland in a World Cup qualifier in 1996?

425. Which other Highland League club were elected to the Scottish League at the same time as Elgin?

426. Do you know the name of Elgin's home ground?

427. Which legendary Scottish international winger briefly played for Elgin in the 1970s?

428. How many times have Elgin been Highland League champions - 8, 14 or 24?

429. What is Elgin's highest League finish since they joined the Scottish League?

430. What are Elgin's official club colours?

# SCOTLAND V. ENGLAND

431. What was the score in the very first Scotland/England international?

432. Following on from the above question, in what year was the match played?

433. Which player broke his leg playing against England in 1963?

434. In what year was the last England/Scotland international played at Wembley?

435. Following on from the above question, who scored Scotland's goal in the match?

436. When was the last time that Scotland beat England at Hampden?

437. Who scored Scotland's goals when they defeated England 3-2 in 1967?

438. Which goalkeeper gave a 'man of the match' performance against England in 1949?

439. At which end of Hampden did Ray Clemence let Kenny Dalglish's shot slip through his legs for Scotland's winning goal against England in 1976?

440. Which player scored a hat-trick for the 'Wembley Wizards' against England in 1928?

# FALKIRK

441.  What is Falkirk's famous nickname?

442.  Do you know the name of Falkirk's previous stadium, where they played for over 100 years?

443.  Can you name the player who missed a penalty in a World Cup semi-final and later played for Falkirk?

444.  How many times have Falkirk won the Scottish Cup?

445.  Which Falkirk legend was voted the club's Player of the Millennium?

446.  Who was the first Falkirk player to win a Scotland cap since John White in 1959?

447.  Which Falkirk player had a goal controversially disallowed in the 1997 Scottish Cup final?

448.  The son of which legendary goalkeeper had a loan spell at Falkirk in 2007?

449.  How many Scotland managers have played for Falkirk?

450.  Following on from the above question, how many can you name?

# NATIONALITIES

*Can you match the following players with the
country of their birth?*

| | | |
|---|---|---|
| 451. | Richard Gough | Singapore |
| 452. | Burton O'Brien | Czech Republic |
| 453. | Shaun Maloney | Ireland |
| 454. | Terry Butcher | Argentina |
| 455. | Gudmunder Torfason | Holland |
| 456. | Willo Flood | France |
| 457. | Sieb Dijkstra | South Africa |
| 458. | Stephane Adam | Malaysia |
| 459. | Gabriel Amato | Iceland |
| 460. | Tomáš Černý | Sweden |

# FORFAR ATHLETIC

461.   What is Forfar's nickname?

462.   Which former Dundee United, Morton and Livingston striker signed for Forfar in June 2008?

463.   In which season did Forfar lose to Rangers in a Scottish Cup semi-final replay?

464.   Which former Rangers and Scotland goalkeeper joined Forfar in 1980?

465.   Which Forfar player received a seventeen match suspension after receiving four red cards in one match?

466.   One of Sir Alex Ferguson's assistant managers at Manchester United began his playing career with Forfar. Who is he?

467.   Who is Forfar's record appearance holder?

468.   Who took over as Forfar's manager in May 2008?

469.   What is the name of Forfar's ground?

470.   Forfar is located in which county?

# TRIVIA - 5

471. What nationality is Hearts' manager Csaba Laszlo?

472. Which player, later to manage Aberdeen, scored the winner in the 1973 English FA Cup final?

473. Who was the first player to captain the winning sides in Scottish and English FA Cup finals?

474. Who is the only Scotsman to have scored in two European Cup finals?

475. Which team signed Tore Andre Flo from Rangers in 2002?

476. In March 2008, which player set a new record as the oldest player to play in the SPL at the age of 42 years and 279 days?

477. Who scored Gretna's goal in the 2006 Scottish Cup final?

478. Against which team did Brian Laudrup score the goal that secured nine in a row for Rangers?

479. Which Scotland player travelled to Argentina for the World Cup even though he was injured and unable to play?

480. Which referee booked Paul Gascoigne after Gazza picked up his yellow card and pretended to book him?

# HAMILTON ACADEMICAL

481. Who is Hamilton's most capped player?

482. Which club did Billy Reid leave to become Hamilton's manager in 2005?

483. Which Hamilton player was the Scottish Football League Young Player of the Year in 2008?

484. Which former Hamilton player scored a hat-trick when playing as a fullback in the 1980s?

485. Which legendary Celtic and Scotland fullback finished his playing career with Hamilton in 1988?

486. Who was Hamilton's top goalscorer when they won the Scottish first division in 2008?

487. Which team did Hamilton beat to earn their first ever victory in the SPL?

488. In how many Scottish Cup finals have Hamilton appeared?

489. Which player scored Hamilton's first goal in the SPL in season 2008/2009?

490. Who was sacked as Hamilton's assistant manager in 2008 after only two months in the job?

# HEART OF MIDLOTHIAN

491. Hearts took their name from the novel The Heart of Midlothian. Can you name the author?

492. How much did Sunderland pay Hearts for Craig Gordon in 2007?

493. Which player holds the Hearts appearance record?

494. Which player has scored more goals against Hibs than any other Hearts player?

495. Can you name the 'Terrible Trio' who played for Hearts in the 1940s and 1950s?

496. How many major honours (League, League Cup and Scottish FA Cup) have Hearts won?

497. Who was the Hearts striker in Scotland's 1974 World Cup pool?

498. How many Hearts players were sent off in a match against Rangers in 1996?

499. Following on from the above question, can you recall who they were?

500. Can you recall the name of the Hearts goalkeeper who was capped six times by Scotland in the 1960s and 1970s?

# STRANGE BUT TRUE

501. Where was Colin Jackson of Rangers and Scotland born?

502. Can you name the Rangers manager who was killed in a boating accident in 1920?

503. For how many senior clubs has Jim Hamilton, currently playing for St Mirren, played?

504. When Kris Boyd signed for Rangers in 2006, what did he do with his signing-on fee?

505. Which player conceded three penalties when playing for Aberdeen against Celtic in 1953?

506. Which Hearts player scored a hat-trick of penalties against Morton in 1973?

507. How many Scottish League Cup finals did Celtic lose in the 1970s?

508. Which player scored over 40 goals in season 1977/1978, but was left out of Scotland's World Cup plans in Argentina?

509. In which city was Brian Laudrup born?

510. Which former Clyde and Dundee player of the 1960s once appeared in a television advert for bread?

# HIBERNIAN

511. Can you name the 'Famous Five' Hibernian forward line of the 1950s?

512. In what year did Hibs last win the Scottish Cup?

513. With which side did former Hibs player and manager Franck Sauzee win a Champions League medal?

514. Can you name the Hibs legend who won 16 Scotland caps and was Scotland's Player of the Year in 1970?

515. What is the record attendance for a Hibs/Hearts derby match, to the nearest 5,000?

516. Which team did Hibernian beat 11-1 in a League match in 1965?

517. Which team did Hibs play in the 2007 Scottish League Cup final and what was the score?

518. How many times have Hibernian played Hearts in a major Cup final?

519. What age was Joe Baker when he played for Hibernian in the 1958 Scottish Cup final - 17, 18 or 19?

520. Which first division side knocked Hibs out of the League Cup in 2008?

# LEGENDS – JOHN GREIG

521. In which city was John Greig born?

522. In what year did John become Rangers' manager?

523. How many Scotland caps did John win?

524. John scored a famous last-minute goal for Scotland in 1965, against which country?

525. Who was Rangers' manager when John signed for the club?

526. In what year did John sign for Rangers?

527. How many trebles (League, Scottish Cup, League Cup) did John win with Rangers?

528. What honour did John receive in 1999?

529. On how many occasions was John voted Scottish Footballer of the Year?

530. Against which country did John make his Scotland debut in 1964?

# INVERNESS CALEDONIAN THISTLE

531. Which two clubs amalgamated to form Inverness Caledonian Thistle?

532. In what year did Inverness Caley famously defeat Celtic in the Scottish Cup at Celtic Park?

533. Following on from the above question, which Celtic player scored an own goal in the match?

534. Who was Caley's first manager after they were elected to the Scottish League?

535. Do you know the club's motto?

536. Caley again knocked Celtic out of the Scottish Cup in 2003. Which player scored the only goal of the match?

537. Can you name the Caley player who was the first Romanian to play for a Scottish club?

538. From which team did Caley sign Don Cowie in 2007?

539. In the 1990s Caley manager Craig Brewster played for Ionikos, a team located in which country?

540. In what year did Caley play their first SPL match?

# VIKING INVASION

*In the 1960s Scottish football was enlivened by an*
*'invasion' of Scandinavian footballers.*
*Can you name the clubs that these players graced?*

541.  Jens Petersen

542.  Mogens Berg

543.  Bent Martin

544.  Per Bartram

545.  Roald Jensen

546.  Finn Dossing

547.  Rene Moller

548.  Preben Arentoft

549.  John Madsen

550.  Henning Boel

# KILMARNOCK

551.  True or false: Kilmarnock are the oldest professional team in Scotland?

552.  Who is Kilmarnock's record appearance holder?

553.  How many times were Kilmarnock Scottish League runners-up between 1960 and 1964?

554.  How many times have Kilmarnock been Scottish Champions?

555.  Who was the Kilmarnock manager when they won the Scottish Cup in 1997?

556.  Following on from the above question, who scored the only goal in the match?

557.  Who is the last Kilmarnock player to have been capped by Scotland?

558.  Can you name the Kilmarnock centre half who won three Scotland caps in the 1960s?

559.  Which player scored five goals for Killie in 1989 against Queen of the South?

560.  Two Killie goalkeepers won Scotland caps in the 1970s. Name them.

# CUP UPSETS

561. Who was the Raith Rovers manager when they won the Scottish League Cup in 1994?

562. Who was the Inverness Caley manager when they knocked Celtic out of the Scottish Cup in 2003?

563. Which player scored twice for second division Morton when they knocked Kilmarnock out of the Scottish Cup in 2007?

564. Partick Thistle defeated Celtic 4-1 in the 1971 League Cup final. What was the half-time score?

565. Which third division side knocked Livingston out of the Scottish Cup in 2008?

566. Which Highland League side knocked Dundee out of the Scottish Cup in 1959?

567. Who scored Hamilton Accie's goal when they knocked Rangers out of the Scottish Cup in 1987?

568. Which famous player played his first game for Celtic in the shock Scottish Cup 2-1 defeat to Clyde in 2006?

569. Following on from the above question, which players scored Clyde's goals in the match?

570. Can you name the player who won the Scottish League Cup finals with Dundee in 1973 and Aberdeen in 1976, both against Celtic?

# LIVINGSTON

571.    By what name were Livingston known until 1974?

572.    By what name were Livingston known from 1974 until 1995?

573.    What is the name of Livingston's home ground?

574.    In what position did Livingston finish in the SPL in season 2001/2002?

575.    Which team did Livingston beat 2-0 in the Scottish League Cup final in 2004?

576.    Following on from the above question, who scored Livvy's goals in the match?

577.    Can you name the Livvy player who played in the 2004 Scottish League Cup final and who was once on the books of Real Madrid?

578.    Can you remember the name of the goalkeeper Celtic signed from Livingston in 2003?

579.    One of Scottish football's most colourful characters has had two spells as Livvy's manager. Can you name him?

580.    Who was sacked as Livingston's manager in June 2008?

# LEGENDS – JIM BAXTER

**581.** In what year was Jim born?

**582.** Do you know the name of Jim's junior side?

**583.** Which team was Jim's first senior club?

**584.** What was the transfer fee when Jim moved to Rangers - £7,500, £17,500 or £27,500?

**585.** How many goals did Jim score against England at Wembley in 1963?

**586.** In 1964 Jim broke his leg playing against which team?

**587.** Which English side did Jim join in 1965?

**588.** For which other English side did Jim play?

**589.** In what year did Jim return to Rangers?

**590.** How many Scotland caps did Jim win?

# MONTROSE

591.  What is the name of Montrose's home ground?

592.  In which year were Montrose formed - 1869, 1879 or 1899?

593.  Do you know Montrose's nickname?

594.  How many Montrose players have been capped for Scotland?

595.  Which legendary Dundee, Spurs and Scotland striker's son played and coached at Montrose?

596.  Which ex-Rangers player resigned as Montrose's manager in 2007?

597.  Jamie Buchan, who signed for Montrose in 2008, has played in the SPL for three different clubs. How many can you name?

598.  Jamie is the son of Scotland defender Martin Buchan. In which city was Jamie born?

599.  Montrose have won only one championship in their history, in season 1984/1985. Which championship did they win?

600.  Can you name the striker who began his career with Montrose in 1961, later played for both Dundee clubs and also won the Scottish Footballer of the Year Award?

# LEGENDS – BILLY McNEILL

601. Can you recall Billy's nickname?

602. How many times did Billy manage Celtic?

603. How many League winners medals did Billy win as a player?

604. For which junior team did Billy play?

605. In how many Scottish Cup finals did Billy score?

606. Which manager signed Billy for Celtic?

607. Which English clubs did Billy manage?

608. How many Scotland caps did Billy win?

609. In what year did Billy win the Scottish Footballer of the Year Award?

610. Which other two Scottish clubs did Billy manage?

# MORTON

611.  Who is Morton's most capped player?

612.  In what year did Morton win their only Scottish Cup?

613.  Following on from the above question, which team did Morton beat in the final?

614.  Which player scored 23 League goals for Morton in 2002/2003 when they won the Scottish third division?

615.  What is Morton's highest ever Premier League finish?

616.  Which player is Morton's record appearance holder?

617.  Which player was freed by Morton in 1983 and was part of Ireland's 1990 World Cup squad?

618.  Which player, who had a loan spell with Morton in 2000, scored a hat-trick against Scotland in 2004?

619.  Against which former England goalkeeper did Andy Ritchie score a hat-trick in 1979?

620.  Which player scored four goals for Morton against Forfar in a second division match in 2007?

# GOALSCORERS

*Can you match the strikers with the clubs where
they are the record goalscorers?*

| | | |
|---|---|---|
| 621. | Joe Harper | Hearts |
| 622. | Allan McGraw | Alloa Athletic |
| 623. | Alan Gilzean | Aberdeen |
| 624. | Kenneth Dawson | Dundee United |
| 625. | Jim Patterson | Morton |
| 626. | Peter MacKay | St Mirren |
| 627. | John Robertson | Falkirk |
| 628. | David McCrae | Dunfermline Athletic |
| 629. | Charlie Dickson | Dundee |
| 630. | Willie Irvine | Queen of the South |

# MOTHERWELL

631. Name the goalkeeper nicknamed the 'Girvan Lighthouse' who began his career with Motherwell.

632. Motherwell's nickname reflects the industrial back ground of the town. What is it?

633. In what year did Motherwell win the Scottish League for the first and (so far) only time?

634. Which player captained Motherwell in the 1991 Scottish Cup final?

635. What was the name given to Motherwell's young side of the 1950s that included future stars such as Ian St John?

636. Who scored Motherwell's winning goal in the 1991 Scottish Cup final?

637. What are Motherwell's official club colours?

638. Which Motherwell legend scored a hat-trick in less than three minutes in 1959?

639. Can you name the famous Motherwell winger who played over 600 matches for the club, scoring more than 250 goals between 1917 and 1937?

640. Can you name the Motherwell forward who scored over 350 career goals, and scored the winning goal in an FA Cup final, yet was never capped by Scotland?

# GOALKEEPERS

641. True or false: Andy Goram never played in a World Cup finals tournament?

642. Who is Scotland's most capped goalkeeper and how many caps did he earn?

643. Which Morton goalkeeper was inducted into Scotland's Hall of Fame in 2007?

644. Which goalkeeper lost nine goals to England in 1961?

645. Which goalkeeper won his first Scotland cap at the age of 36?

646. Name the goalkeeper who scored on his debut for Aberdeen in 1981?

647. Which goalkeeper broke with protocol and kissed a member of the royal family prior to a Scottish Cup final?

648. How many Scotland caps did television presenter Bob Wilson win?

649. From which side did Celtic sign Artur Boruc?

650. Two Aberdeen goalkeepers won Scotland caps in the same season (1969/1970). Can you name them?

# PARTICK THISTLE

651.    Can you name Partick Thistle's most capped player?

652.    Thistle's most famous match is their 4-1 victory over Celtic in the 1971 Scottish League Cup final. Can you recall the four players who scored Thistle's goals?

653.    Following on from the above question, who was Thistle's captain in the match?

654.    How many different spells as manager of Partick Thistle did John Lambie have?

655.    The record crowd for a Partick Thistle home match is 49,838 in 1922. Who were Thistle's opponents on that day?

656. Can you remember the name of the fullback that Thistle transferred to Manchester United in 1972?

657.    Thistle signed two goalkeepers from Rangers in the 1960s. Can you remember who they were?

658.    How many spells did Chic Charnley have as a Thistle player?

659.    Who was Thistle's manager when they won the Scottish League Cup in 1971?

660.    In which season did Thistle last play in the SPL?

# HISTORY

661. Who was the last player to score in three successive Scottish Cup finals?

662. Which player holds the Scottish career record for the most goals?

663. Can you name the four players who have scored five goals in a Scottish Premier League match?

664. Who is the only Scottish player to have won the European Golden Boot?

665. Who was the first Scottish player to win England's Player of the Year Award?

666. How many European Champions finals have been held at Hampden Park?

667. Which Scotsman is the only player/manager to have won the English League and Cup double?

668. Which player scored four goals in the 1960 European Cup final at Hampden?

669. For how many seasons in a row did East Stirling finish bottom of the third division before 2007/2008?

670. Who is the last player to have scored a hat-trick in a Scottish Cup final?

# PETERHEAD

671. In what year were Peterhead admitted to the Scottish League?

672. What is the name of Peterhead's home ground?

673. Do you know Peterhead's nickname?

674. To which team did Peterhead lose on the last day of the 2002/2003 season to deny Peterhead promotion to the Scottish second division?

675. Which ex-Aberdeen player took over as Peterhead's manager in 2008?

676. Can you name the giant defender who was part of the Inverness Caley Thistle side that knocked Celtic out of the Scottish Cup and who joined Peterhead in 2007?

677. Which player scored the winning goal for Peterhead against Morton in the Scottish Cup in 2008?

678. Can you name the player who was voted Peterhead's Cult Hero in 2005?

679. Which Dundee United player, who won his first Scotland cap in 2008, spent a season on loan with Peterhead?

680. Which Hibs player, now a full international, was briefly on loan to Peterhead in 2000?

# SEASONS - 2002/2003

681. Rangers won the SPL in this season by the narrowest of margins. What was their winning margin?

682. Which side did Rangers defeat 6-1 in their last match to take the title?

683. True or false: Rangers won the domestic treble of League, League Cup and Scottish Cup?

684. Which side were Scottish Cup runners-up?

685. Which two English sides did Celtic knock out on their way to the UEFA Cup final?

686. Which Dundee player scored his only goal for Scotland (so far) against Iceland in 2003?

687. Which player won the Players' Player of the Year and the Writers' Player of the Year?

688. Which player missed a penalty for Celtic against Kilmarnock in the last match of the season?

689. Dundee United had three managers in this season. How many can you name?

690. Which future Scotland star won the Young Player of the Year Award for 2002/2003?

# QUEEN OF THE SOUTH

691. Can you name the Queen of the South player who is credited in the Guinness Book of Records as scoring the fastest hat-trick in British football?

692. How old was Ally McLeod when he played for Queen of the South in a reserve match in 1992?

693. Prior to the final in 2008, what was Queen's best performance in the Scottish Cup?

694. Which side did Queen beat in the semi-final to reach the Scottish Cup final in 2008?

695. Following on from the above question, who scored Queen's winning goal in the match?

696. Which player scored from inside his own half in the Scottish Cup tie against in 2008?

697. Which famous 'Wembley Wizard' began his career with Queen of the South?

698. Who was the long-serving Queen goalkeeper who played over 800 games for the club?

699. Who were Queen's first opponents in European football?

700. Who scored Queen's first goal in European competition?

# MANAGERS' FIRST CLUBS

*Do you know at which clubs these Scottish managers began their playing careers?*

701.  Jimmy Calderwood

702.  Craig Levein

703.  Craig Brewster

704.  Derek McInnes

705.  Owen Coyle

706.  Mark McGhee

707.  David Irons

708.  Bobby Williamson

709.  Billy Stark

710.  Ian McCall

# QUEENS PARK

711. True or false: Queens Park have twice been runners-up in the English FA Cup final?

712. How many times have Queens Park won the Scottish Cup?

713. What is Queens Park's motto?

714. Which team did Queens Park beat in the 2006/2007 play-off final to win promotion to the second division?

715. Many famous footballers began their careers at Queens Park. Which Lisbon Lion made his debut for Queens Park aged 14?

716. Which Queens Park player was the first black player to be capped by Scotland?

717. Three Scotland managers began their playing career with Queens Park. Can you name them?

718. Which SPL club did Queens Park knock out of the CIS League Cup in 2006?

719. What is Queens Park's nickname?

720. Who was head coach at Queens Park prior to Gardner Speirs?

# SCOTTISH CLUBS IN EUROPE

721. Which were the first Scottish club to play in Europe?

722. Following on from the above question, which round did they reach?

723. Can you name the two Dundee United players who scored seven goals between them in a UEFA Cup match in 1997?

724. Which German side did Dundee United thrash 5-0 in the 1981/1982 UEFA Cup?

725. Which player supplied the cross for John Hewitt to score the winning goal for Aberdeen in the 1983 European Cup Winners Cup final?

726. Which team did Morton play in their only season in European competition?

727. True or false: Dundee and Dundee United have both reached the semi-finals of the European Cup?

728. Which player scored four goals for Celtic in a European Cup Winners Cup match in 1989?

729. Against which team did Henrik Larsson break his leg in 1999?

730. Which team did Rangers play in their first European final?

# RAITH ROVERS

**731.** Which famous 'Wembley Wizard' with the baggy shorts began his career with Raith?

**732.** What was the score after extra time when Raith Rovers won the Scottish League Cup in 1994?

**733.** Following on from the above question, who scored Raith's goals in the match?

**734.** Can you name the former Dundee United and Scotland player who played in the above match for Raith at the age of 38?

**735.** Which French international's brother was briefly Raith's manager in 2004?

**736.** Which Rovers manager left the club within a week of his appointment to manage Dundee United?

**737.** How many League goals did Raith score in season 1937/1938?

**738.** Which English commentator was responsible for the immortal phrase 'And they will be dancing in the streets of Raith tonight'?

**739.** Which famous German side did Raith Rovers play in their only season in European competition?

**740.** Which member of Aston Villa's 1982 European Cup winning side was the son of a Raith Rovers legend?

# SCOTTISH AND FA CUP DOUBLES

*These players have won the FA Cup in both Scotland
and England. Can you match the players with the clubs
they won the trophies with?*

| | |
|---|---|
| 741. Gordon Strachan | **Hearts and Spurs** |
| 742. Brian McClair | **Rangers and Everton** |
| 743. Martin Buchan | **Kilmarnock and Sheffield Wednesday** |
| 744. Gary Stevens | **Rangers and Spurs** |
| 745. Ronnie Simpson | **Aberdeen and Manchester United** |
| 746. Alex Young | **Celtic and Manchester United** |
| 747. Lou Macari | **Aberdeen and Manchester United** |
| 748. Paul Gascoigne | **Celtic and Newcastle** |
| 749. Joe Nibloe | **Hearts and Everton** |
| 750. Dave MacKay | **Celtic and Manchester United** |

# RANGERS

751. What is Rangers' motto?

752. In season 1898/1899 Rangers won every League match they played. How many games did they play?

753. In what year did Rangers play the famous Russian side Moscow Dynamo in a challenge match?

754. How many hat-tricks did Ally McCoist score for Rangers?

755. Which player scored twice for Rangers when they won the European Cup Winners Cup in 1972?

756. Who is Rangers' record appearance holder?

757. Who was Graeme Souness's first signing for Rangers?

758. Which Rangers 'great' played 11 times against England in the home internationals?

759. Which Rangers manager's father played for Blackpool for 14 years?

760. Which Rangers player scored four goals against Valetta in the UEFA Cup in 1983?

# PAST MASTERS

761.   From which team did Brian Laudrup sign for Rangers?

762.   How many goals did Ally McCoist score for Scotland?

763.   Who is the only player to win the Scottish League with three different clubs outwith Celtic and Rangers?

764.   Following on from the above question, can you name the three clubs?

765.   Which legendary Hearts centre forward was inducted into Scotland's Hall of Fame in 2007?

766.   Danny McGrain was manager of which club in the 1990s?

767.   Which Scottish international was known as 'The Ghost of White Heart Lane'?

768.   Can you name the former Hearts and Spurs great whom Brian Clough signed for Derby County?

769.   How many Scottish League Cup winners medals did Davie Cooper win with Rangers?

770.   With which club did Graeme Souness begin his playing career?

# ROSS COUNTY

771.  Which town do Ross County hail from?

772.  Do you know the name of County's home ground?

773.  In what year were County admitted to the Scottish League?

774.  Which former Rangers and England striker ended his playing career with Ross County?

775.  Which side did Ross County defeat to win the 2006 Scottish Challenge Cup?

776.  True or false: Ross County are the most northerly League Club in Scotland?

777.  Which former Northern Ireland international signed for County in 2008?

778.  Which Premiership side signed 16-year-old Alex Cooper from County in 2007?

779.  What is Ross County's nickname?

780.  Who was appointed Ross County's manager in October 2007?

# THOSE WE HAVE LOST

*Scottish football is littered with clubs whose demise has caused much heartache to their fans.*
*How much can you remember about those we have lost?*

781. How many seasons did Clydebank spend in the Premier League?

782. How many championships did Gretna win in their short tenure in Scottish football?

783. Morton's local rivals in their early years were another Clydeside club. Who were they?

784. Can you name the team from Dunbartonshire who won the Scottish Cup three times in the 1870s?

785. Can you name the other Dunbartonshire club who won the Scottish Cup twice in the 1880s, and claimed the title of 'Champions of the World'?

786. What was the name of the famous Glasgow team who played at Cathkin Park?

787. In which city were St Bernards FC based?

788. Which famous Rangers and Scotland winger began his career with Clydebank?

789. Which famous Third Lanark goalkeeper won 16 Scotland caps prior to World War I?

790. Which player scored the goal to clinch Gretna's promotion to the SPL in 2007?

# ST JOHNSTONE

791.  Which two St Johnstone managers also managed Scotland?

792.  What was the name of St Johnstone's ground prior to moving to McDiarmid Park?

793.  Can you name the former Rangers midfielder who also managed Airdrie and began his playing career with St Johnstone?

794.  How much did St Johnstone receive from Blackburn Rovers for Calum Davidson in 1998?

795.  Which German side did Saints defeat in the 1971/1972 UEFA Cup?

796.  What is Saints' highest Premier League finish?

797.  In which season did St Johnstone last play in the SPL?

798.  Which Soviet Union international played for Saints in the 1990s?

799.  Who scored both goals when Saints knocked Rangers out of the Scottish League Cup in 2006?

800.  Which SPL club did Saints defeat in the Scottish Cup in 2008?

# WHO AM I?

*Can you identify these Scottish players and
managers from the clues?*

801.   I was a cultured central defender who represented
       Scotland in the 1990 World Cup. Now a manager, I
       have developed a penchant for criticising Scottish
       referees.

802.   I was a Scottish international who captained Arsenal's
       1970/1971 double side.

803.   I am an SPL manager who shares the same name (and
       nickname) as a Celtic great.

804.   I am the grandson of a Celtic legend and I have 53
       Scotland caps.

805.   I played for St Mirren, Leeds and Manchester United
       and briefly managed Airdrie.

806.   I began my career with The Dons and was a Scottish
       Cup winner aged 17. I won 11 Scotland caps and also
       played for Leeds and Manchester United. My
       nickname was Bumper.

807.   I spent my entire career with Liverpool and won 29
       caps for Scotland, and I was a Justice of the Peace.

808.   My nickname was 'Last Minute' and I won 38 Scotland
       caps.

809.   I was named after a singer and entertainer and I
       almost signed for Leeds United. I played under Brian
       Clough at Notts Forest.

810.   I captained Newcastle and Scotland and managed an
       Edinburgh club.

# ST MIRREN

811. How many times have St Mirren won the Scottish Cup?

812. In what year did St Mirren beat Aberdeen in the Scottish Cup final?

813. Which player scored the last ever League goal at the old St Mirren Park (Love Street) before the club moved to their new ground in January 2009?

814. Who replaced Alex Ferguson as St Mirren's manager?

815. Who scored the winning goal for St Mirren in the 1987 Scottish Cup final?

816. Which St Mirren manager was Lawrie McMenemie's coach at Southampton?

817. The record attendance for a St Mirren home match is 47,438 in 1949. Who were the opponents?

818. Which St Mirren player is married to glamour model Michelle Marsh?

819. Which division three club knocked St Mirren out of the Scottish League Cup in 2007?

820. Who was the last St Mirren player to be capped by Scotland?

# TRANSFERS

821. Which player was the subject of the first six-figure transfer in Scottish football?

822. Which player did Falkirk sign in 1922 for a reported world record transfer fee?

823. Celtic signed Scott Brown from Hibernian in 2007 to break the Scottish transfer record. How much did Celtic pay?

824. Which player nicknamed 'The Bonnie Prince' did Dundee sign from Aberdeen in 1964 for £40,000?

825. Which Morton player was transferred to Derby County for £15,500 in 1947 for a then British record fee?

826. To the nearest £50,000, how much did Celtic pay Feyenoord for Henrik Larsson?

827. How much did Spurs pay for Alan Hutton in 2008?

828. Which former Dundee United player was transferred for £1,469,000 in 1979?

829. Which player did Aberdeen pay £1,000,000 for in 1995 from Oldham Athletic?

830. How much did Arsenal pay Rangers for Giovanni van Bronckhorst in 2001?

# STENHOUSEMUIR

831. What is Stenhousemuir's claim to fame regarding floodlights?

832. Which Scandinavian country has a branch of the Stenhousemuir Supporters' Club?

833. Stenhousemuir won the Challenge Cup in 1995, beating which team in the final?

834. Following on from the above question, what was the score in the match?

835. Which Premier League side did Stenny knock out of the 1996 Scottish Cup?

836. What is Stenhousemuir's nickname?

837. Which Stenhousemuir manager became famous for the type of coat he wore?

838. Which teenager was transferred from Stenhousemuir to Hearts in 2007?

839. In what year did Stenny beat Rangers at Ibrox in a Scottish League Cup match?

840. Who was appointed manager of Stenhousemuir in October 2007?

# THE OLD FIRM

841. How many times have Celtic and Rangers met in the Scottish Cup final?

842. What was unusual about the 1909 Scottish Cup final between the two clubs?

843. Which player scored a hat-trick for Rangers in the 1983 Scottish League Cup final?

844. Which player scored two penalties against Rangers in the 1965 Scottish League Cup final?

845. What was the score in the 1957 Scottish League Cup final between the two sides?

846. Which player scored Rangers' winning goal in the 1966 Scottish Cup final against Celtic?

847. In what year did the very first Old Firm match take place?

848. Who scored the only goal of the 1999 Scottish Cup final between the clubs?

849. How many goals did Ally McCoist score in Old Firm matches?

850. What was the score in Martin O'Neill's first ever Old Firm match in 2000?

# STIRLING ALBION

851. In what year were Stirling Albion formed?

852. Stirling Albion's original ground shared the name of which famous English club?

853. What was the score when Stirling defeated Selkirk in the Scottish Cup in 1984?

854. Following on from the above question, which player scored seven goals in the match?

855. What was the name of the town of Stirling's original League club?

856. What was the nickname given to the club in their early years thanks to their many promotions and relegations?

857. Can you name the goalkeeper who moved from Stirling to Everton in 2003?

858. Can you name the former Stirling Albion player who made over 1,000 career appearances? (Clue – he also played for Stenhousemuir and Meadowbank.)

859. Can you recall Stirling's long-serving manager who was in charge from 1974 to 1986?

860. Stirling's record goalscorer shares the name of a Scottish rugby star of the 1970s and a famous Scottish footballer of the 1940s. Who is he?

# PLAYERS' NICKNAMES

*Can you identify the former Scottish international footballers from their nicknames?*

861.   **Wispy**

862.   **Corky**

863.   **Juke Box**

864.   **The Cannonball Kid**

865.   **Luggy**

866.   **Stroller**

867.   **The Wee Barra**

868.   **Choccy**

869.   **Big Eck**

870.   **The King**

# STRANRAER

871. Which competition did Stranraer win in season 1996/1997?

872. Following on from the previous question, which side did Stranraer defeat in the final?

873. And who scored the winning goal in the above final?

874. Which player was voted Stranraer's all-time Cult Hero in 2005?

875. How many times did Stranraer win the Scottish second division in the 1990s?

876. Which former Celtic striker, who played in the 1970 European Cup final, briefly managed Stranraer in the 1970s?

877. Which current Kilmarnock defender began his career with Stranraer?

878. In which year were Stranraer founded – 1870, 1880 or 1890?

879. What are Stranraer's official club colours?

880. In what position in division three did Stranraer finish in 2007/2008?

# SPORTING YEAR

*Can you identify the year by the clues?*

881.  David Bowie was number 1 in the charts and Gordon Strachan scored his first Scotland goal.

882.  Rangers won the treble and the film Jaws was scaring everyone out of the water.

883.  It was the summer of love and Scotland's greatest football year.

884.  Maggie came to power and the Scottish Cup final went to three games.

885.  Roger Federer won Wimbledon for the first time and Gretna were elected to the Scottish League.

886.  Paul Lawrie won the Open Golf Championship and Alex Ferguson was knighted.

887.  Gordon Strachan was appointed Celtic's manager and Hedgehunter won The Grand National.

888.  Alan Wells won an Olympic gold medal and the Old Firm Cup final ended in a riot.

889.  The World Cup was held in Italy and Aberdeen won the Scottish Cup 9-8 on penalties.

890.  Fulham reached the English Cup final and Airdrie were beaten finalists in the Scottish Cup.

# SCANDALS

891. For which club was Willie Johnston playing when he was sent home from the 1978 World Cup?

892. Can you name the 'Copenhagen Five' who were banned from playing for Scotland for life in 1975?

893. Who were the two St Johnstone footballers sacked in 2001?

894. Which Scottish manager claimed on oath that all managers were liars?

895. Which Raith Rovers player did Duncan Ferguson headbutt in 1994, resulting in Ferguson being jailed?

896. Which former Celtic goalkeeper was jailed for his part in the British football betting scandal of 1964?

897. Who was the Scottish referee who was suspended by the SFA for receiving gifts from AC Milan before a UEFA cup tie?

898. Which teammate did Craig Levein punch during a Hearts match, earning himself a lengthy ban?

899. Who were the three players charged by the police in the aftermath of an Old Firm game in 1987?

900. In what year was Jim Farry sacked as SFA Chief Executive over the Jorge Cadete affair?

# SCOTLAND

901. Scotland have competed in how many European Championship finals?

902. In which year did Scotland first qualify for the European Championship finals?

903. Scotland were drawn against the same country in the qualifying stages of the 1974 and 1978 World Cup finals. Can you name the country?

904. Who was the first Scottish player ordered off the pitch in a Scotland international?

905. Which player scored the goal in Scotland's 1-0 victory over France at Hampden in 2006?

906. Who was the last player to score a hat-trick for Scotland?

907. Which famous centre forward scored 23 goals in only 20 games for Scotland?

908. Who was the last player to score a hat-trick for Scotland against England?

909. Which player scored his only goal for Scotland against the then World Cup holders in 1990?

910. Which player scored Scotland's last ever goal in the home international tournament?

# RED CARDS

911. Against which country did Andy Gray receive a red card when playing for Scotland in 1976?

912. Which Hearts player was ordered off the pitch in the 1986 Scottish Cup final?

913. How many players were ordered off the pitch in the Old Firm Scottish Cup match in 1991?

914. Following on from the above question, how many can you name?

915. Which Scottish player was red carded against Morocco in 1998?

916. Which player did Tommy Gemmell chase and then kick in the posterior, earning himself an early bath when playing for Scotland against West Germany in 1969? (Clue – he played against England in that match in 1966.)

917. Which Celtic player was shown a red card in the 1986 Scottish League Cup final, but was allowed to stay on the park?

918. Which Rangers player was red carded in his last ever match for them in 2008?

919. Which Rangers player was banned indefinitely in the 1950s after the fourth dismissal of his career?

920. Which Hamilton Accies player was red carded against both Celtic and Rangers in 2008?

# EXPERT LEGENDS

921. How many goals in total did Denis Law score for Scotland against England?

922. Which famous Englishman was Bill Shankly's footballing hero?

923. Which player did Matt Busby sign from Celtic in 1963?

924. How many European Cups did Kenny Dalglish win with Liverpool?

925. Which England player swapped jerseys with Jimmy Johnstone after he had memorably destroyed the English at Hampden in 1974?

926. For which team was Alex Ferguson playing when he was dropped for the 1965 Scottish Cup final?

927. How many times in total did John Greig and Billy McNeill win the Scottish League as players?

928. Against which country did Kenny Dalglish equal Denis Law's Scotland goals record?

929. Jock Stein returned to one of his former clubs, Dunfermline, to sign which midfielder in 1968?

930. Which player did Bill Shankly sign from Dundee United in 1961?

# FOREIGN MASTERS

931. How many times did Henrik Larsson finish as top goalscorer in the SPL?

932. How many career goals did Henrik Larsson score in the SPL?

933. From which team did Rangers sign Arthur Numan?

934. Can you remember the name of the Argentinian striker who had a successful spell at Dundee - Fabian _____?

935. Can you recall Finland's captain who played for Morton in the 1990s?

936. Who was the Dutch striker who won a Scottish Cup winners medal with Aberdeen in 1990?

937. With which club did Brian Laudrup finish his playing career?

938. Which French player scored for Hearts against Rangers in the 1998 Scottish Cup final?

939. Who was the Swedish winger, famous for his dead ball shooting, who played for Dundee United and Rangers in the 1960s?

940. For which two Portuguese clubs has Russell Latapy played?

# THE SPL

941. Who were the first SPL champions and in which season?

942. Who is the highest goalscorer in the SPL's history?

943. Who was the first sponsor of the SPL?

944. What is the record number of points won by a club in the SPL in a single season?

945. How many points did Gretna win in season 2007/2008?

946. Who was the top scorer in the SPL in season 2007/2008?

947. Which two sides were involved in an eleven-goal thriller in season 1999/2000?

948. For how many clubs has Stevie Crawford played in the SPL?

949. Which club has won the most SPL titles, and how many?

950. Who is the only non-Celtic player to have finished as SPL top scorer for a season?

# EXPERT HISTORY

951.  Which Scottish manager who was involved in a famous Cup upset in Scotland also played for Bedford Town when they knocked Newcastle out of the FA Cup in 1964?

952.  How many Rangers players were included in England's 1990 World Cup squad?

953.  Following on from the above question, how many can you name?

954.  Can you name the seven players who played in both of Celtic's European Cup finals?

955.  Can you name the four players who played in Rangers' European Cup Winners finals of 1967 and 1972?

956.  In what year was the first Scottish Cup final played at the present Hampden?

957.  Following on from the above question, who were the teams in that match?

958.  In the above match, which player scored a hat-trick?

959.  Which Scotland player scored the 500th goal in the history of the World Cup finals at the 1958 tournament?

960.  Where was the first Scotland/England international match played?

# EXPERT SCOTLAND IN THE WORLD CUP

961. Which two Norwich City players were included in Scotland's 1990 World Cup finals squad?

962. Which player was fouled in the build-up to Scotland's penalty in the 1990 World Cup group match against Sweden?

963. How many players did Scotland take with them to the 1954 World Cup finals?

964. How many goals did Ally McCoist score in World Cup final tournaments?

965. What was the name of the Uruguayan player who was red carded against Scotland in 1986?

966. Can you name the Dundee United players in the 1986 World Cup finals squad?

967. Can you name the Dundee goalkeeper who was included in the 1974 World Cup squad?

968. Can you name the two English-born goalkeepers in the 1998 World Cup squad?

969. Which player scored Scotland's first ever goal in the World Cup finals?

970. Which player has made the most appearances for Scotland in World Cup finals tournaments? 3

# EXPERT SCOTTISH CLUBS
# IN EUROPE

971. Who was the first Scottish player to be sent off in a European match?

972. Which father and son have both been sent off in European matches?

973. Which player scored the first goal by a Scottish side in European competition?

974. Which team did Gretna face in their only season in European football?

975. How many games did Rangers play to reach the UEFA Cup final in 2008 (not including the final)?

976. How many Scottish clubs have participated in European competition (up to 2007/2008)?

977. Which St Mirren player scored a hat-trick in the UEFA Cup in 1985?

978. Which players scored Celtic's goals against Leeds in their 3-1 aggregate victory in the 1970 European Cup semi-final?

979. How many Scottish clubs have played in all three major European competitions?

980. Following on from the above question, how many can you name?

# EXPERT TRIVIA

981.  In 1960 a St Mirren played scored 10 goals in a Scottish Cup match and in 1961 his brother scored 9 goals for Hibs in a Scottish Cup match. Can you name the brothers?

982.  Which player is credited with giving birth to 'The Hampden Roar'?

983.  Who was the Scottish international nicknamed 'The Golden Vision' who played for Everton in the 1960s?

984.  Who was the first player outwith the Old Firm to win the Football Writers' Player of the Year?

985.  Who was the last Scotsman to score in the English FA Cup final?

986.  Who is the only player to have scored a hat-trick in a Scottish Cup and Scottish League Cup final?

987.  Who is the only player to have won the Footballer of the Year Award in England and Scotland?

988.  In which city did Scotland lose to Costa Rica in the 1990 World Cup finals?

989.  Can you name the five Scottish clubs whose names begin and end with the same letter?

990.  Can you name the four players who played in all four of Aberdeen's victorious Scottish Cup finals from 1982 to 1986?

# EXPERT SCOTLAND

991. Who was the South African-born fullback who played for Scotland in the 1950s?

992. Which famous Scotland captain was once memorably described as 'ten stones of barbed wire'?

993. How many times did Scotland win the home international tournament outright?

994. Which two Liverpool players have both twice scored own goals when playing for Scotland?

995. Two Welshmen have scored hat-tricks against Scotland. Can you name them?

996. After Rangers and Celtic, which club has had the most players capped for Scotland?

997. The youngest player to be capped for Scotland shares the same name as an ex-Partick Thistle manager. Can you name him?

998. Which Rangers legend captained Scotland on 48 occasions?

999. Which country did Scotland beat 5-1 in the 2006 Kirrin Cup competition?

1000. How many caps did Tommy Burns win for Scotland?

# ANSWERS

## BEGINNINGS

| 1. | Joe Jordan | Morton |
| 2. | Gary Gillespie | Falkirk |
| 3. | Alan Hansen | Partick Thistle |
| 4. | Steve Nicol | Ayr United |
| 5. | Gordon McQueen | St Mirren |
| 6. | Pat Nevin | Clyde |
| 7. | George Wood | East Stirling |
| 8. | Allan Evans | Dunfermline Athletic |
| 9. | Graeme Sharp | Dumbarton |
| 10. | Alex Cropley | Hibernian |

## SCOTLAND AT THE WORLD CUP

11. Brazil
12. John Wark
13. Bruce Rioch
14. 5
15. Billy Bremner, Peter Lorimer, Joe Jordan, Gordon McQueen and David Harvey
16. Joe Jordan
17. Teofilo Cubillas
18. 4
19. Uruguay
20. Alex Ferguson

## ABERDEEN

21. 7
22. Eric Black and John Hewitt
23. True
24. SV Hamburg
25. They adopted red shirts for the first time

26. *George Hamilton (against Belgium in 1951)*

27. *Andrew Considine (son of Doug)*

28. *Dave Robb*

29. *Joe Harper*

30. *Aberdeen 10, KR Reykjavik 0*

## LEGENDS – DENIS LAW

31. *Aberdeen*

32. *Huddersfield Town, Manchester City (twice) and Manchester United*

33. *False. Denis missed the 1968 final through injury*

34. *1 (1974)*

35. *1964*

36. *Torino*

37. *4*

38. *Zaire*

39. *55*

40. *30*

## AIRDRIEONIANS/AIRDRIE UNITED

41. *Ian McMillan*

42. *The Diamonds*

43. *Hughie Gallacher*

44. *1924*

45. *2*

46. *Kenny Black*

47. *Steve Archibald*

48. *Drew Busby and Drew Jarvie*

49. *Clydebank*

50. *Gretna were placed in administration, losing their place in the Scottish League. The leagues were*

restructured and Airdrie as runners-up in the play-offs were promoted to the first division

## LEGENDS – BILL SHANKLY

51. 1913
52. Cherrypickers
53. Bob Shankly
54. England
55. Preston North End
56. Carlisle United
57. 1959
58. 1964
59. The 1974 Charity Shield
60. Liverpool Reserves

## ALBION ROVERS

61. Jock Stein
62. 1
63. John (Jock) White
64. Bernie Slaven
65. Tony Green
66. 40
67. Sam Malcolmson
68. New Zealand
69. Vic Kasule
70. The semi-final

## BIRTH YEARS

| 71. | Aberdeen | 1903 |
|-----|----------|------|
| 72. | Dunfermline | 1885 |
| 73. | East Stirlingshire | 1881 |

| 74. | Elgin City | 1893 |
|---|---|---|
| 75. | Hamilton Academical | 1874 |
| 76. | Hibernian | 1875 |
| 77. | Morton | 1874 |
| 78. | Motherwell | 1886 |
| 79. | Queens Park | 1867 |
| 80. | Stirling Albion | 1945 |

## ALLOA ATHLETIC

81. Clackmannan County
82. 1921
83. John White
84. Tommy Hutchison
85. Recreation Park
86. 1 (Jock Hepburn)
87. £100,000
88. Willie Crilley (49 in season 1921/1922)
89. They lost in the play-off semi-finals to Clyde 6-5 on aggregate
90. Selkirk

## HOME GROUNDS

| 91. | Albion Rovers | Cliftonhill |
|---|---|---|
| 92. | Arbroath | Gayfield |
| 93. | Ayr United | Somerset Park |
| 94. | Cowdenbeath | Central Park |
| 95. | Dunfermline Athletic | East End Park |
| 96. | Kilmarnock | Rugby Park |
| 97. | Raith Rovers | Stark's Park |
| 98. | St Johnstone | McDiarmid Park |
| 99. | Stenhousemuir | Ochilview |

100.   Stranraer                                  Stair Park

## ANNAN ATHLETIC
101.   1942
102.   Cowdenbeath
103.   Annan 4, Cowdenbeath 1
104.   Galabank
105.   Arbroath
106.   Davie Irons
107.   Derek Townsley
108.   Mike Jack
109.   Dumfries and Galloway
110.   Black and gold

## CLUB NICKNAMES
| | | |
|---|---|---|
| 111. | Alloa Athletic | The Wasps |
| 112. | Arbroath | The Red Lichties |
| 113. | Clyde | The Bully Wee |
| 114. | Dumbarton | The Sons |
| 115. | Dundee United | The Arabs |
| 116. | Dunfermline Athletic | The Pars |
| 117. | East Fife | The Fifers |
| 118. | Partick Thistle | The Jags |
| 119. | Queen of the South | The Doonhamers |
| 120. | St Mirren | The Buddies |

## ARBROATH
121.   36-0 (against Aberdeen Bon Accord)
122.   1885
123.   35-0 (Dundee Harp 35, Aberdeen Rovers 0)
124.   John Petrie

125. **Montrose**

126. **Steve Kirk**

127. **Ned Doig (2 caps)**

128. **Dave Smith, Andy Penman and Willie Mathieson**

129. **Stranraer**

130. **It is the closest football ground to the sea in British senior football**

## NAME THE YEAR

131. **1986**

132. **2002**

133. **1979**

134. **1988**

135. **1967**

136. **2004**

137. **1994**

138. **2000**

139. **1952**

140. **1989**

## AYR UNITED

141. **'Tam o' Shanter'**

142. **The Honest Men**

143. **2002 (Scottish League Cup final)**

144. **Rangers**

145. **Gordon Dalziel**

146. **Neil McBain (aged 52 at the time)**

147. **66**

148. **Johnny Doyle**

149. **Wigan Athletic**

150. **John Murphy**

## TRIVIA - 1

151.  3

152.  Chris Sutton

153.  Robbie Winters

154.  Roger Hynd

155.  Morton

156.  Kilmarnock: Willie Kilmarnock

157.  Bobby Williamson

158.  Paul Lambert

159.  Archie Gemmill (for St Mirren, 1966)

160.  He scored direct from a corner kick. The referee disallowed the goal, but Tully then repeated the act and this time the goal stood

## BERWICK RANGERS

161.  Jock Wallace

162.  Sammy Reid

163.  Jerry Kerr

164.  Peterhead

165.  Eric Tait

166.  The Borderers

167.  Shielfield Park

168.  Dave Smith

169.  Jimmy Crease

170.  Jim Jeffries

## SEASONS – 1966/1967

171.  Kilmarnock

172.  Leeds United

173.  Stevie Chalmers

174.  Roger Hynd

175. Morton
176. Ronnie Simpson
177. Dukla Prague
178. Jim Craig
179. John Greig
180. Willie Wallace

## BRECHIN CITY

181. Hamilton Accies
182. Morton
183. 4
184. Charlie Adam
185. Glebe Park
186. Shamrock Rovers
187. 3
188. Ian Campbell
189. 1906
190. The Hedgemen

## SIR ALEX FERGUSON

191. Queens Park
192. Dunfermline, £65,000
193. Ayr United
194. St Mirren
195. Billy McNeill
196. 3
197. 1986
198. 1990 FA Cup
199. Henrik Larsson
200. 1999

## CELTIC

201.  42
202.  Willie Maley
203.  Kenny Dalglish, Danny McGrain, Paul McStay, Tom Boyd, John Collins, Roy Aitken and John Thomson
204.  Tommy Gemmell
205.  Ronnie Simpson
206.  Jimmy Johnstone
207.  Patsy Gallacher
208.  Tommy Docherty
209.  Frank McAvennie
210.  John (Dixie) Deans

## QUOTE/UNQUOTE

211.  Walter Smith
212.  Alex McLeish
213.  Alex Totten
214.  Andy Roxburgh
215.  Alan Brazil
216.  Lorenzo Amoruso (after a 'spat' with Ayr United's James Grady)
217.  Murdo MacLeod
218.  Gordon Strachan
219.  Tommy Docherty
220.  Andy Gray

## CLYDE

221.  Cumbernauld
222.  Shawfield Stadium
223.  3
224.  John Clark and Billy McNeill

225. Craig Brown

226. Archie Robertson (in 1955)

227. Steve Archibald

228. Airdrie United

229. Harry Haddock

230. Tommy Ring (with 12)

## MACS

231. Ted MacDougall (for Bournemouth)

232. Derek McKay

233. Frank McAvennie

234. Gary McSwegan

235. Ross McCormack

236. Ronnie McKinnon

237. Jackie McNamara

238. Stephen McGinn

239. Malcolm MacDonald

240. Malky Mackay

## TRIVIA - 2

241. Ivan Sproule

242. John Fleck (for Rangers, in 2008, aged 16 years and 274 days)

243. St Johnstone

244. John Robertson for Notts Forest

245. The Iron Curtain

246. 1995/1996 (Scottish League Cup)

247. 1964/1965

248. Inverness Caledonian Thistle

249. Bill Brown, Dave McKay and John White

250. Bruce Rioch

## SEASONS – 1977/1978

251. Rangers
252. Aberdeen
253. Morton
254. Derek Johnstone
255. Don Masson and Kenny Dalglish
256. Anfield
257. Dave Jones
258. 5th
259. Clydebank
260. Don Masson

## COWDENBEATH

261. Craig Levein
262. Jim Baxter
263. Hookey
264. 16
265. 3
266. 3
267. Alex Venters
268. The Blue Brazil
269. Craig Gordon
270. Mixu Paatelainen

## LEGENDS - JIMMY JOHNSTONE

271. 1944
272. Jinky
273. Stanley Matthews
274. 1963
275. 23
276. 2

277. Terry Cooper
278. Flea
279. Athletico Madrid
280. Dundee

## DUMBARTON

281. 1872
282. 2
283. 6
284. 1
285. Alex Jackson
286. Walter Smith
287. Joe Coyle, Tommy Coyle and Owen Coyle
288. Boghead
289. Tom McAdam and Colin McAdam
290. Dumbarton Rock

## LEGENDS – JOCK STEIN

291. 1922
292. Centre half
293. Miner
294. Wales
295. Albion Rovers
296. Dunfermline Athletic
297. Hibernian
298. 1965 Scottish Cup
299. Leeds United
300. 1978

## DUNDEE

301. 1893

302. *1910*

303. *Albert Juliussen*

304. *Billy Steel for £23,500*

305. *1962/1963*

306. *AC Milan*

307. *Gordon Wallace*

308. *Tommy Gemmell against Celtic*

309. *2003*

310. *Fabrizio Ravanelli*

## TRIVIA - 3

311. *Hugh Sproat*

312. *1998/1999*

313. *Roman Bedner*

314. *Rangers, Hibernian and Dundee*

315. *Jim Forrest*

316. *Valdas Ivanauskas*

317. *Alan Gilzean*

318. *John McGovern*

319. *Airdrie*

320. *Denis Law*

## DUNDEE UNITED

321. *Hibernian*

322. *Hamish McAlpine*

323. *David Goodwillie*

324. *Jerry Kerr*

325. *Dave Narey*

326. *6*

327. *Barcelona*

328. *3*

329. He was never cautioned

330. AS Roma

## SEASONS – 1987/1988

331. Billy McNeill

332. Dundee United

333. Frank McAvennie (2)

334. Morton

335. Paul McStay

336. Dunfermline Athletic

337. Colombia

338. Hamilton Accies

339. Tommy Coyne

340. 3 (Falkirk, Dunfermline and Morton)

## LEGENDS - SIR MATT BUSBY

341. 1909

342. Liverpool and Manchester City

343. 1945

344. 1958

345. The Busby Babes

346. Denis Law

347. 5

348. Benfica

349. False. He won one cap

350. 1968

## DUNFERMLINE ATHLETIC

351. Norrie McCathie

352. East Fife

353. Jock Stein

354. Celtic

355. Pat Gardner

356. Tommy and Willie Callaghan

357. 29

358. Allan Evans

359. Istvan Kozma

360. Jim Leishman

## THE SCOTTISH CUP

| | | |
|---|---|---|
| 361. | Morton | 1922 |
| 362. | Partick Thistle | 1921 |
| 363. | St Mirren | 1926 |
| 364. | Third Lanark | 1905 |
| 365. | Motherwell | 1991 |
| 366. | Dumbarton | 1883 |
| 367. | Airdrieonians | 1924 |
| 368. | Dundee United | 1994 |
| 369. | St Bernards | 1895 |
| 370. | Falkirk | 1913 |

## EAST FIFE

371. 1927

372. 1938

373. Kilmarnock

374. 3

375. Scot Symon

376. Henry Morris

377. Goran Stanic

378. Paul McManus

379. Henry McLeish

380. Charlie Fleming

## TRIVIA - 4

| | | |
|---|---|---|
| 381. | Danny McGrain | 62 |
| 382. | Alan Rough | 53 |
| 383. | Gordon Strachan | 50 |
| 384. | Derek Johnstone | 14 |
| 385. | Dave Narey | 35 |
| 386. | John Collins | 58 |
| 387. | Willie Miller | 65 |
| 388. | David Provan (Celtic) | 10 |
| 389. | Asa Hartford | 50 |
| 390. | Duncan Ferguson | 7 |

## SEASONS – 1997/1998

391. Celtic
392. Marco Negri
393. Kjell Oloffson
394. Hibernian
395. Dundee
396. Hearts
397. Wim Jansen, managing Celtic
398. David Hopkin
399. 1
400. Jackie McNamara

## EAST STIRLINGSHIRE

401. 117
402. Pointless
403. 8
404. Eddie McCreadie
405. John Hartson
406. Rangers 6, East Stirlingshire 0

407. *1962/1963*
408. *Gordon Russell*
409. *Norway*
410. *East Stirling Clydebank*

## LEGENDS – KENNY DALGLISH

411. *Jock Stein*
412. *112*
413. *Belgium*
414. *Tommy Docherty*
415. *3: 1974, 1978 and 1982*
416. *£440,000 in 1977*
417. *102*
418. *30*
419. *Denis Law*
420. *Rangers*

## ELGIN CITY

421. *2000*
422. *Morton*
423. *Alan Main*
424. *John McGinlay*
425. *Peterhead*
426. *Borough Briggs*
427. *Jimmy Johnstone*
428. *14*
429. *5th in Division Three*
430. *Black and white*

## SCOTLAND V. ENGLAND

431. *Scotland 0, England 0*

432. *1872*
433. *Eric Caldow*
434. *1999*
435. *Don Hutchison*
436. *1985*
437. *Denis Law, Bobby Lennox and Jim McCalliog*
438. *Jimmy Cowan*
439. *The East Terracing (the Celtic end)*
440. *Alex Jackson*

## FALKIRK

441. *The Bairns*
442. *Brockville*
443. *Chris Waddle*
444. *2*
445. *Kevin McAllister*
446. *Darren Barr*
447. *Neil Oliver*
448. *Peter Schmeichel, father of Kasper*
449. *6*
450. *John Prentice, Bobby Brown, Willie Ormond, Alex Ferguson, Andy Roxburgh and Craig Brown*

## NATIONALITIES

451. *Richard Gough*           *Sweden*
452. *Burton O'Brien*          *South Africa*
453. *Shaun Maloney*          *Malaysia*
454. *Terry Butcher*           *Singapore*
455. *Gudmunder Torfason*   *Iceland*
456. *Willo Flood*             *Ireland*
457. *Sieb Dijkstra*           *Holland*

| 458. | Stephane Adam | France |
|------|---------------|--------|
| 459. | Gabriel Amato | Argentina |
| 460. | Tomáš Černý | Czech Republic |

## FORFAR ATHLETIC

461. The Loons
462. Derek Lilley
463  1981/1982
464. Stewart Kennedy
465. Dave Bowman
466. Archie Knox
467. Ian McPhee
468. Dick Campbell
469. Station Park
470. Angus

## TRIVIA - 5

471. Hungarian
472. Ian Porterfield
473. Martin Buchan
474. Tommy Gemmell
475. Sunderland
476. Andy Millen (St Mirren)
477. Ryan McGuffie
478. Dundee United
479. Gordon McQueen
480. Dougie Smith

## HAMILTON ACADEMICAL

481. Colin Miller (29 caps for Canada)
482. Clyde

483. James McCarthey

484. John Brown

485. Danny McGrain

486. Richard Offiong

487. Dundee United in 2008

488. 2

489. Tony Stevenson

490. John McCormack

## HEART OF MIDLOTHIAN

491. Sir Walter Scott

492. £9,000,000

493. Gary Mackay

494. John Robertson

495. Alfie Conn, Willie Bauld and Jimmy Wardhaugh

496. 15

497. Donald Ford

498. 4

499. David Weir, Neil Pointon, Paul Ritchie and Pasquale Bruno

500. Jim Cruickshank

## STRANGE BUT TRUE

501. London

502. William Wilton

503. 9

504. He donated half of it to Kilmarnock's Youth and Development Department

505. Jimmy Mitchell

506. Donald Ford

507. 7

508. Derek Johnstone

509. Vienna

510. Joe Gilroy

## HIBERNIAN

511. Gordon Smith, Bobby Johnstone, Lawrie Reilly, Eddie Turnbull and Willie Ormond

512. 1902

513. Olympique Marseille

514. Pat Stanton

515. 65,860

516. Hamilton Accies

517. Kilmarnock. Hibs won 5-1

518. 1 (1896 Scottish Cup final)

519. 17

520. Morton

## LEGENDS – JOHN GREIG

521. Edinburgh

522. 1978

523. 44

524. Italy

525. Scot Symon

526. 1961

527. 3 (1963/1964, 1975/1976 and 1977/1978)

528. He was voted the Greatest Ever Rangers Player by the club's fans

529. 2 (1966 and 1976)

530. England

## INVERNESS CALEDONIAN THISTLE

531. Caledonian FC and Inverness Thistle FC
532. 2000
533. Lubo Moravcik
534. Sergei Baltacha
535. ' The Pride of the Highlands'
536. Dennis Wyness
537. Marius Niculae
538. Ross County
539. Greece
540. 2004

## VIKING INVASION

541. Aberdeen
542. Dundee United
543. Dunfermline
544. Morton
545. Hearts
546. Dundee United
547. Hearts
548. Morton
549. Morton and Hibs
550. Aberdeen

## KILMARNOCK

551. True (founded in 1869)
552. Alan Robertson (1972-1988)
553. 4
554. 1 (1964/1965)
555. Bobby Williamson
556. Paul Wright

557.	Steven Naismith (in 2007)

558.	Jackie McGrory

559.	Willie Waters

560.	Ally Hunter and Jim Stewart

## CUP UPSETS

561.	Jimmy Nicholl

562.	John Robertson

563.	Chris Templeman

564.	Partick 4, Celtic 0

565.	East Stirlingshire

566.	Fraserburgh

567.	Adrian Sprott

568.	Roy Keane

569.	Eddie Malone and Craig Bryson

570.	Jocky Scott

## LIVINGSTON

571.	Ferranti Thistle

572.	Meadowbank Thistle

573.	Almondvale

574.	3rd

575.	Hibernian

576.	Derek Lilley and Jamie McAllister

577.	Oscar Rubio

578.	Javier Broto

579.	Jim Leishman

580.	Mark Proctor

## LEGENDS – JIM BAXTER

581.	1939

582. Crossgates Primrose
583. Raith Rovers
584. £17,500
585. 2
586. Rapid Vienna
587. Sunderland
588. Notts Forest
589. 1969
590. 34

## MONTROSE

591. Links Park
592. 1879
593. The Gable Endies
594. 2
595. Ian Gilzean, son of Alan
596. David Robertson
597. Aberdeen, Dundee United and Partick Thistle
598. Manchester
599. The Scottish second division
600. Gordon Wallace

## LEGENDS – BILLY McNEILL

601. Caesar
602. 2
603. 9
604. Blantyre Victoria
605. 3 (1965, 1969, 1972)
606. Jimmy McGrory
607. Aston Villa and Manchester City
608. 29

609. *1965*

610. *Clyde and Aberdeen*

## MORTON

611. *Jimmy Cowan (25 caps)*

612. *1922*

613. *Rangers*

614. *Alex Williams*

615. *6th (1979/1980)*

616. *Derek Collins*

617. *Bernie Slaven*

618. *Robert Earnshaw*

619. *Peter Bonetti*

620. *Peter Weatherson*

## GOALSCORERS

| | | |
|---|---|---|
| 621. | *Joe Harper* | *Aberdeen* |
| 622. | *Allan McGraw* | *Morton* |
| 623. | *Alan Gilzean* | *Dundee* |
| 624. | *Kenneth Dawson* | *Falkirk* |
| 625. | *Jim Patterson* | *Queen of the South* |
| 626. | *Peter MacKay* | *Dundee United* |
| 627. | *John Robertson* | *Hearts* |
| 628. | *David McCrae* | *St Mirren* |
| 629. | *Charlie Dickson* | *Dunfermline Athletic* |
| 630. | *Willie Irvine* | *Alloa Athletic* |

## MOTHERWELL

631. *Peter McCloy*

632. *The Steelmen*

633. *1932*

634. Tom Boyd

635. The Ancell Babes

636. Steve Kirk

637. Claret and amber

638. Ian St John

639. Bobby Ferrier

640. Hughie Ferguson

## GOALKEEPERS

641. True

642. Jim Leighton (with 91)

643. Jimmy Cowan

644. Frank Haffey

645. Ronnie Simpson

646. Marc de Clerck (against Berwick Rangers)

647. John Martin (of Airdrie)

648. 2

649. Legia Warsaw

650. Bobby Clark and Ernie McGarr

## PARTICK THISTLE

651. Alan Rough (with 51)

652. Alex Rae, Bobby Lawrie, Dennis McQuade and Jimmy
     Bone

653. Alex Rae

654. 3

655. Rangers

656. Alex Forsyth

657. Billy Ritchie and George Niven

658. 3

659. Davie McParland

660.   2003/2004

## HISTORY

661.   Bobby Lennox
662.   Jimmy McGrory
663.   Paul Sturrock, Kenny Miller, Marco Negri and Kris Boyd
664.   Ally McCoist (in 1992)
665.   Bobby Collins (in 1965)
666.   3 (1960, 1976, and 2002)
667.   Kenny Dalglish
668.   Ferenc Puskas
669.   5
670.   Gordon Durie (for Rangers, against Hearts, in 1996)

## PETERHEAD

671.   2000
672.   Balmoor
673.   The Blue Toon
674.   Morton
675.   Neale Cooper
676.   Bobby Mann
677.   Martin Bavidge
678.   John Sievwright
679.   Scott Robertson
680.   Garry O'Connor

## SEASONS -2002/2003

681.   One goal
682.   Dunfermline
683.   True
684.   Dundee

685. *Liverpool and Blackburn Rovers*

686. *Lee Wilkie*

687. *Barry Ferguson*

688. *Alan Thompson*

689. *Alex Smith, Paul Hegarty and Ian McCall*

690. *James McFadden*

## QUEEN OF THE SOUTH

691. *Tommy Bryce (December 1993 against Arbroath)*

692. *61*

693. *Semi-final (twice)*

694. *Aberdeen*

695. *John Stewart*

696. *Ryan McCann*

697. *Hughie Gallacher*

698. *Allan Ball*

699. *FC Nordsjaelland*

700. *Sean O'Connor*

## MANAGERS' FIRST CLUBS

701. *Birmingham*

702. *Cowdenbeath*

703. *Forfar*

704. *Morton*

705. *Dumbarton*

706. *Bristol City*

707. *Queen of the South*

708. *Clydebank*

709. *St Mirren*

710. *Queens Park*

## QUEENS PARK

711. True
712. 10
713. 'Ludere causa Ludendi' - to play for the sake of playing
714. East Fife
715. Ronnie Simpson
716. Andrew Watson
717. Alex Ferguson, Andy Roxburgh and Bobby Brown
718. Aberdeen
719. The Spiders
720. Billy Stark

## SCOTTISH CLUBS IN EUROPE

721. Hibernian (in 1955)
722. Semi-final of the European Cup
723. Robbie Winters (4) and Gary McSwegan (3). Dundee United beat CE Principat 8-0
724. Borussia Moenchengladbach
725. Mark McGhee
726. Chelsea
727. True
728. Dariusz Dziekanowski
729. Lyon
730. Fiorentina (in the 1961 European Cup Winners Cup)

## RAITH ROVERS

731. Alex James
732. 2-2 (against Celtic)
733. Steve Crawford and Gordon Dalziel
734. Dave Narey

735. Nicolas Anelka

736. Tommy McLean

737. 142

738. Sam Leitch

739. Bayern Munich

740. Ken McNaught, son of Raith great Willie McNaught

## SCOTTISH AND FA CUP DOUBLES

| | | |
|---|---|---|
| 741. | Gordon Strachan | Aberdeen and Manchester United |
| 742. | Brian McClair | Celtic and Manchester United |
| 743. | Martin Buchan | Aberdeen and Manchester United |
| 744. | Gary Stevens | Rangers and Everton |
| 745. | Ronnie Simpson | Celtic and Newcastle |
| 746. | Alex Young | Hearts and Everton |
| 747. | Lou Macari | Celtic and Manchester United |
| 748. | Paul Gascoigne | Rangers and Spurs |
| 749. | Joe Nibloe | Kilmarnock and Sheffield Wednesday |
| 750. | Dave MacKay | Hearts and Spurs |

## RANGERS

751. 'Ready'

752. 18

753. 1945

754. 28

755. Willie Johnston

756. John Greig

757. Colin West

758. Alan Morton

759. Jock Wallace (father Jock Wallace senior)

760. Dave McPherson

## PAST MASTERS

761. Fiorentina

762. 19

763. Gordon Smith

764. Hibs, Hearts and Dundee

765. Willie Bauld

766. Arbroath

767. John White

768. Dave MacKay

769. 7

770. Tottenham Hotspur

## ROSS COUNTY

771. Dingwall

772. Victoria Park

773. 1994

774. Mark Hateley

775. Clyde

776. True

777. Danny Griffin

778. Liverpool

779. The Staggies

780. Derek Adams

## THOSE WE HAVE LOST

781. 3

782. 3
783. Port Glasgow Athletic
784. Vale of Leven
785. Renton FC
786. Third Lanark
787. Edinburgh
788. Davie Cooper
789. Jimmy Brownlie
790. James Grady

## ST JOHNSTONE

791. Bobby Brown and Willie Ormond
792. Muirton Park
793. Alex MacDonald
794. £1.75 million
795. SV Hamburg
796. 3rd (1998/1999)
797. 2001/2002
798. Sergei Baltacha
799. Steven Milne
800. St Mirren

## WHO AM I?

801. Craig Levein
802. Frank McLintock
803. John Hughes (Yogi)
804. Kevin Gallacher
805. Gordon McQueen
806. Arthur Graham
807. Billy Liddell
808. Lawrie Reilly

809. Asa Hartford

810. Bobby Moncur

## ST MIRREN

811. 3

812. 1959

813. Craig Dargo (against Hamilton Accies in December 2008)

814. Rikki McFarlane

815. Ian Ferguson

816. Jim Clunie

817. Celtic

818. Will Haining

819. East Fife

820. Roy Aitken

## TRANSFERS

821. Colin Stein

822. Syd Puddefoot

823. £4.4 million

824. Charlie Cooke

825. Billy Steel

826. £650,000

827. £9 million

828. Andy Gray (Aston Villa to Wolves)

829. Paul Bernard

830. £8.5 million

## STENHOUSEMUIR

831. Stenhousemuir's home game against Hibernian in November 1951 was the first match in Scotland to be

*played under floodlights*

832. Norway

833. Dundee United

834. 0-0. Stenny won 5-4 on penalties

835. Falkirk

836. The Warriors

837. Terry Christie (duffel coat)

838. David Templeton

839. 1972

840. John Coughlin


## THE OLD FIRM

841. 15

842. The final went to a replay, which also ended in a draw. The SFA decided not to play extra time, resulting in the fans rioting, and the trophy was withheld

843. Ally McCoist

844. John Hughes

845. Celtic 7, Rangers 1

846. Kai Johansen

847. 1888

848. Rod Wallace

849. 27

850. Celtic 6, Rangers 2


## STIRLING ALBION

851. 1945

852. Annfield (Anfield for Liverpool)

853. 20-0

854. Davie Thompson

855. Kings Park

856. The Yo Yos
857. Iain Turner
858. Graeme Armstrong
859. Alex Smith
860. Billy Steele

## PLAYERS' NICKNAMES

861. Willie Wallace
862. George Young
863. Gordon Durie
864. Charlie Nicholas
865. Paul Sturrock
866. George Graham
867. Bobby Collins
868. Brian McClair
869. Alex McLeish
870. Denis Law

## STRANRAER

871. The League Challenge Cup
872. St Johnstone
873. Tommy Sloan
874. Lex Grant
875. 2
876. John Hughes
877. Fraser Wright
878. 1880
879. Blue and white
880. 2nd

## SPORTING YEAR

881.   1980
882.   1976
883.   1967
884.   1979
885.   2002
886.   1999
887.   2005
888.   1980
889.   1990
890.   1975

## SCANDALS

891.   West Bromwich Albion
892.   Billy Bremner, Joe Harper, Pat McCluskey, Willie Young and Arthur Graham
893.   George O'Boyle and Kevin Thomas
894.   Tommy Docherty
895.   Jock McStay
896.   Dick Beattie
897.   John Gordon
898.   Graham Hogg
899.   Terry Butcher, Chris Woods and Frank McAvennie
900.   1999

## SCOTLAND

901.   2
902.   1992
903.   Czechoslovakia
904.   Billy Steel (against Austria in 1951)
905.   Gary Caldwell

906. *Colin Stein (4 goals, against Cyprus, in 1969)*
907. *Hughie Gallacher*
908. *Alex Jackson (in 1928)*
909. *Stewart McKimmie (against Argentina)*
910. *Mark McGhee (against England, in 1984)*

## RED CARDS

911. *Czechoslovakia*
912. *Walter Kidd*
913. *4*
914. *Terry Hurlock, Mark Hateley, Mark Walters and Peter Grant*
915. *Craig Burley*
916. *Helmut Haller*
917. *Tony Shepherd*
918. *Daniel Cousin*
919. *Willie Woodburn*
920. *Martin Canning*

## EXPERT LEGENDS

921. *3*
922. *Tom Finney*
923. *Pat Crerand*
924. *3*
925. *Peter Shilton*
926. *Dunfermline Athletic*
927. *14*
928. *Spain (in 1984)*
929. *Tommy Callaghan*
930. *Ron Yeats*

## FOREIGN MASTERS

931.  5

932.  158

933.  PSV Eindhoven

934.  Caballero

935.  Janne Lindberg

936.  Hans Gillhaus

937.  Ajax Amsterdam

938.  Stephane Adam

939.  Orjan Persson

940.  FC Porto and Boavista


## THE SPL

941.  Rangers in 1998/1999

942.  Henrik Larsson

943.  The Bank of Scotland

944.  103 (Celtic in 2001/2002)

945.  13

946.  Scott McDonald (Celtic)

947.  Motherwell and Aberdeen (final score Motherwell 5, Aberdeen 6)

948.  4 (Hibernian, Dunfermline, Dundee United and Aberdeen, plus Raith Rovers in the old Premier Division)

949.  Celtic, 6

950.  Kris Boyd (twice)


## EXPERT HISTORY

951.  Jock Wallace

952.  4

953.  Gary Stevens, Terry Butcher, Chris Woods and Trevor

Steven

954. Tommy Gemmell, Bobby Murdoch, Billy McNeill, Jimmy Johnstone, Willie Wallace, Bertie Auld and Bobby Lennox

955. Sandy Jardine, John Greig, Dave Smith and Willie Johnston

956. 1904

957. Celtic and Rangers

958. Jimmy Quinn (of Celtic)

959. Bobby Collins

960. West of Scotland cricket ground in Hamilton Crescent, Glasgow

## EXPERT SCOTLAND IN THE WORLD CUP

961. Robert Fleck and Bryan Gunn

962. Roy Aitken

963. 13

964. None

965. Jose Batista

966. Dave Narey, Eamonn Bannon, Paul Sturrock, Richard Gough and Maurice Malpas

967. Thomson Allan

968. Neil Sullivan and Jonathon Gould

969. Jimmy Murray (of Hearts, against Yugoslavia, in 1958)

970. Jim Leighton (with 9)

## EXPERT SCOTTISH CLUBS IN EUROPE

971. Jimmy Logie (of Rangers, against Nice, in 1956)

972. Jackie McInally and Alan McInally

973. Eddie Turnbull (for Hibs, in 1955 against Rott Weiss Essen)

974. Derry City

975. 18

976. 18

977. Brian Gallacher (against Hammarby)

978. George Connolly, John Hughes and Bobby Murdoch

979. 8

980. Celtic, Rangers, Kilmarnock, Dundee United, Aberdeen, Hearts, Dundee and Hibernian

## EXPERT TRIVIA

981. Gerry Baker (10) for St Mirren against Glasgow University and Joe Baker (9) for Hibs against Peebles Rovers)

982. Alec Cheyne (when he scored direct from a corner against England in 1929)

983. Alex Young

984. Gordon Wallace (Raith Rovers, 1968)

985. Brian McClair (for Man United in 1994)

986. John (Dixie) Deans

987. Gordon Strachan (although Kenny Dalglish won the English award in 1979 and was also part of the 1974 World Cup squad who were given the award en masse in 1974)

988. Genoa

989. Celtic, Dundee United, East Fife, East Stirlingshire and Kilmarnock

990. Jim Leighton, Willie Miller, Neale Cooper and Alex McLeish

## EXPERT SCOTLAND

991. John Hewie

992.  *Billy Bremner*

993.  *24 (plus 17 shared)*

994.  *Gary Gillespie and Steve Nicol*

995.  *John Toshack and Robert Earnshaw*

996.  *Queens Park (with 80)*

997.  *John Lambie (of Queens Park)*

998.  *George Young*

999.  *Bulgaria*

1000. *8*

# BOOK REVIEWS:

*"Want to test your knowledge from caps to cups and from legends to leagues? Then get your hands on 'The Scottish Football Quiz Book'. Quality, fun and a must for footy fans."*

**- Raman Bhardwaj, STV News**

*"The ultimate test of knowledge for any diehard Scottish football fan. Find out who REALLY knows their stuff!"*

**- Ian Simpson, Moray Firth Radio**

*"Guaranteed to invoke heated debate, even a stramash - in the pub."*

**- Sally McNair, BBC Scotland**

*"A must for very football encyclopediac."*

**- Keith Downie, Setanta Sports**

# BOOK REVIEWS:

*"I think this is BRILLIANT, it is just brilliant to see so much about ALL of the scottish teams. Brilliant fun that I'm sure people will learn so much from."*

**- Steve Courtney, Central 103.1 FM**

*"What an absolute gem of trivia - I loved the different categories and questions ... and I actually knew a few answers as well! A huge amount of research has gone into this book and what a result! It's been great fun going through it."*

**- Alison Walker, BBC Scotland**

*"Those of us who are Scottish football fans know it's not the despair that gets to you - it's the hope. This is enough to cheer us all up. A must-have for any serious fan - and for the not so serious fan too."*

**- Gavin Esler, BBC Newsnight**

*"Ever stuck with things to say at the pub? Worry no more - the ultimate footie book is here to make you seem interesting. Hours of eye brow raising fun and facts."*

**- Stuart Webster, Tay FM**

# BOOK REVIEWS:

*"I thought I knew a lot about Scottish football until I read this, now I'm not so sure!"*

**- Scott Wilson, Radio Forth 2**

*"Perfectly pitched for both the casual football fan, and the complete anorak."*

**- Jonathan Sutherland, BBC Scotland**

*"Featuring every SPL and SFL club, no Scottish football fan should feel left out!"*

**- Jim Gellatly, BBC Radio Scotland**

*"If you have even a passing interest in Scottish Football ... this book will make you a fan for life."*

**- Frank Adam, Moray Firth Radio**

*"As a football fan, I found this quiz book great fun. You can pick it up anytime and test your football knowledge and surprise yourself with what you do or don't know about the beautiful game."*

**- Billy Anderson, GMG Radio**

# BOOK REVIEWS:

*"This is a fascinating quiz book which is well researched and presented. Football fans all over (not just in Scotland) will spend many hours enjoying it as well as learning a host of interesting facts about Scottish Football."*

**- Stuart Cameron, Sky Sports**

*"Thoroughly excellent. It shows Statto who's boss!"*

**- Ruth Davidson, BBC Radio Scotland 92.4 FM**

*"A doorway into Scottish football trivia heaven! Everything you know, want to know and thought you knew is here. Enjoy!"*

**- Gerry McCulloch, STV**

*"Most of my questions on Scottish football are about Alan Rough, like: How did he ever manage to turn up for a game on time? However, here you have a book full of interest for all fans of the beautiful game in Scotland."*

**- Jay Crawford, GMG Radio**

*"You will know more than you think you knew and discover you know less than you thought you knew! What a book!"*

**- Ciarán O'Toole, Rock Radio**

# BOOK REVIEWS:

*"A true compendium of Scottish Football knowledge and a must for any fan wanting to test their knowledge! Covering every inch of the beautiful game from your favorite team, club, and players! A quick ready through and get prepared to win a lot of arguments! If only every pub in Scotland had one behind the bar!"*
**- Sam Turner, Super Station Orkney**

*"The question is: Why have we waited so long for this?"*
**- James Pilu, West 96.7 FM**

*"Ideal trivia for matchday banter - as essential to the Scottish fan as pie, bovril and novelty tartan hat!"*
**- Bruce McKenzie, West Sound Radio**

*"If you think you know about football – get this book and prepare for the biggest challenge of your life!"*
**- Mike Richardson, Radio Tay**

*"A great way to spend a boring Sunday afternoon! I am doing my Xmas shopping early and buying this for my brothers!"*
**- Gina McKie, Radio Clyde**

# BOOK REVIEWS:

*"This is the very book for Scottish Football fans, it's full of all the answers you're looking for."*

**- Keith Thomson, Radio Forth & Radio Tay**


*"A fascinating book of Scottish teams and legends a must for all football fans and quiz hosts."*

**- Ian Young, West Sound Radio 1035 AM**


*"What an excellent quiz book an essential item if you are creating a quiz night or radio competition."*

**- David Ogg, Nevis Radio**


*"If you thought you knew all about Scottish Football, then think again. Everybody can learn new facts and stats."*

**- Graeme Logan, Leith 98.8 FM**


*"An excellent read that deserves a place on every bookshelf."*

**- Ryan Woodman, Super Station Orkney**

# BOOK REVIEWS:

*"Morton fan Graeme Ross has come up with another winner ... now Scottish football fans can test their knowledge in his latest book that provides hours of fun and facts."*
**- Stewart Peterson, Greenock Telegraph**

*"A great football book, with plenty for fans of every team - perfect for those long away-day bus journeys!"*
**- Kieran Westbrook, Dumfries and Galloway Standard**

*"No Scottish football fan should leave the house without it."*
**- Iain Robertson, Alloa & Hillfoots Advertiser**

*"Almost as satisfying as a half-time pie and bovril, and infinitely more readable."*
**- Kevin Janiak, The Southern Reporter**

*"This is a must read for members of the Tartan Army or indeed any football fanatic."*
**- John Riddle, The Paper**

# BOOK REVIEWS:

*"A great journey through time as well as an entertaining way of finding out how much you know about the beautiful game."*

**- Frank Cassidy, Ayr Advertiser**

*"The typical Scottish football fan loves nothing more than debating about the game whether it's in the pub or at the match. This book is perfect for it, with great questions on every team in the country."*

**- Scott McDermott, Sunday Mail**

*"This splendid book is certainly the answer for those of us who like quizzes and have an interest in football North of the border."*

**- David Powter, Winger Magazine**

*"This will kick off endless hours of heated debate between football fans from Aberdeen to Stranraer. A referee may well be required."*

**- Robert Leslie, Orkney Today**

*"A cracking book which is sure to appeal to fans everywhere, whether they support Arbroath or Aberdeen, Raith Rovers or Rangers!"*

**- Brian Stormont, Arbroath Herald**

www.apexpublishing.co.uk